CW00662886

Crafting Connections.

Contemporary Applied Behavior Analysis
for Enriching the Social Lives of
Persons with Autism Spectrum Disorder

Autism Partnership

Mitchell Taubman, Ph.D.

Ron Leaf, Ph.D.

John McEachin, Ph.D.

With contributions by
Marlene Driscoll, M.A., LMFT

B. J. Freeman, Ph.D.

Alyne Kuyumjian, M.S.

Justin Leaf, Ph.D.

Karen McKinnon, M. Ed. Psych.

Tracee Parker, Ph.D.

Julia Peacock, M.S.

Jon Rafuse, M.A.

Julide Saltuklaroglu

Andrea Waks, J.D., M.A.

To Ivar

Crafting Connections: Contemporary Applied Behavior Analysis for Enriching the Social Lives of Persons with Autism Spectrum Disorder

Book Layout: PreMediaGlobal
Cover Art: Aldo Murillo/iStockphoto.com; Zlatko Kostic/iStockphoto.com; Catherine Yeulet/iStockphoto.com
Cover models used for illustrative purposes only.

Library of Congress Control Number: 2010933759
ISBN: 978-0-9755859-9-3

Contents

About the Authors

Mitchell Taubman, Ph.D.

Mitchell Taubman worked with Dr. Ivar Lovaas as an undergraduate at the University of California at Los Angeles (UCLA) in the early 1970s. He treated children with autism, attention-deficit/hyperactivity disorder (ADHD), and other disorders. He then attended the University of Kansas, studying with such founders of applied behavior analysis (ABA) as Dr. Donald Baer, Dr. Todd Risely, Dr. James Sherman, and his doctoral advisor, Dr. Montrose Wolf. After completing his Ph.D., Dr. Taubman returned to UCLA and served as an Adjunct Assistant Professor of psychology and as co-principal investigator with Dr. Lovaas on a federal grant concerned with autism treatment. One of his special interests is Teaching Interactions, which he brought from the Kansas model to autism treatment. After his postdoctoral work, Dr. Taubman obtained his license as a clinical psychologist and served as clinical director of Straight Talk, a program providing residential and day treatment services to adults with autism and other developmental disabilities. He currently serves as Co-Director of Autism Partnership, where he provides treatment oversight, training, and consultation around the world. Dr. Taubman is the co-author of *It's Time for School! Building Quality ABA Educational Programs for Students with Autism Spectrum Disorders* and *Sense and Nonsense in the Behavioral Treatment of Autism: It Has to Be Said*.

Ronald Leaf, Ph.D.

Ronald Leaf is a licensed psychologist who has more than 30 years of experience in the field of autism. Dr. Leaf began his career working with Professor Ivar Lovaas, while receiving his undergraduate degree at the University of California at Los Angeles (UCLA). Subsequently, he received his doctorate under the direction of Dr. Lovaas. During his professional training at UCLA, he served as Clinic Supervisor, Research Psychologist, Lecturer, and Interim Director of the Young Autism Project. He was extensively involved in many of the Young Autism Project research investigations, contributed to *The Me Book,* and is co-author of *The Me Book Videotapes,* a series of instructional tapes offering training for teaching autistic children. He is co-author of *A Work in Progress* (a manual on behavioral treatment of autism), *It's Time for School! Building Quality ABA Educational Programs for Students with Autism Spectrum Disorders,* and *Sense and Nonsense in the Behavioral Treatment of Autism: It Has to Be Said.* Dr. Leaf has consulted nationally and internationally to families, school districts, day programs, and residential treatment facilities. He served as the Director of Straight Talk's Developmental Disabilities Services division for 15 years; this program provided residential and day treatment for adults with developmental disabilities. Dr. Leaf is also the Executive Director of Behavior Therapy and Learning Center, a mental health agency providing treatment, consultation, and related services to parents, program staff, and school personnel in the United States.

John McEachin, Ph.D.

John McEachin is a licensed psychologist who has been providing behavioral intervention to children with autism as well as adolescents and adults with a wide range of developmental disabilities for more than 35 years. He received his graduate training under Professor Ivar Lovaas at the University of California at Los Angeles (UCLA) on the Young Autism Project. During his 11 years at UCLA, Dr. McEachin served in various roles, including Clinic Supervisor, Research and Teaching Assistant, Visiting Professor, and Acting Director. His research has included a long-term follow-up study of young autistic children who received intensive behavioral treatment, the results of which were published in 1993. Since receiving his Ph.D. in clinical psychology in 1987, his work has included serving as Clinical Director of Developmental Disabilities Services, a division of Straight Talk in Signal Hill, California. Dr. McEachin has lectured throughout the world and consulted to numerous families and agencies, assisting in the development of treatment programs and providing training to parents, group home staff, and classroom personnel. In 1994, he joined with Ron Leaf in forming Autism Partnership, which they co-direct. In 1999, they co-authored a book on applied behavior analysis for persons with autism, titled *A Work in Progress*. In 2008, they published *It's Time for School! Building Quality ABA Educational Programs for Students with Autism Spectrum Disorders* and *Sense and Nonsense in the Behavioral Treatment of Autism: It Has to Be Said*.

Marlene Driscoll, M.A., LMFT

Marlene Driscoll is a Licensed Marriage and Family Therapist specializing in work with families of children with autism. She has more than 20 years of experience in the field of developmental disabilities, and is currently the Site Director for the Autism Partnership Seal Beach office. As Site Director, Ms. Driscoll provides clinical supervision, program development, and mentoring. She began working with Drs. Leaf and McEachin in 1992 as a consultant for the Behavior Therapy and Learning Center, which focused on parent training for families with developmentally disabled children. She earned her master's degree in counseling from Loyola Marymount University in 1996. Ms. Driscoll has brought her knowledge of behavioral intervention and autism together with her therapeutic training to provide counseling services for individuals and families impacted by ASD-related concerns. She has extensive experience in the use of applied behavior analysis and early intervention with children with autism. She has consulted with families and school districts throughout the United States and internationally.

B. J. Freeman, Ph.D.

B. J. Freeman is Professor Emerita of Medical Psychology at the University of California at Los Angeles (UCLA) School of Medicine. She is Founder and past Director of the UCLA Autism Evaluation Clinic, and co-founder of UCLA's Early Childhood Partial Hospitalization Program. Dr. Freeman is considered an international authority in the diagnosis, psychological assessment, and treatment of children and adults with autism spectrum disorders, and has published more than 100 articles in scientific journals and books in the area of autism. After retiring from UCLA, Dr. Freeman has continued to practice in the Los Angeles area. She spends much of her professional time working with families and service organizations, and consulting with school districts to develop appropriate educational programs for children with autism.

Alyne Kuyumjian, M.S.

Alyne Kuyumjian has worked with Drs. Mitch Taubman, Ron Leaf, and John McEachin at Autism Partnership since 2005. She earned her bachelor's degree in psychology from the University of California, Riverside. She received her master of science degree in applied behavior analysis from St. Cloud State University. Currently, Ms. Kuyumjian is a Program Coordinator at Autism Partnership, providing supervision for students' programming and training to staff members. In addition, she provides consultation and training to school districts and families throughout the United States.

Justin Leaf, Ph.D.

Justin Leaf completed his Ph.D. at the University of Kansas under the mentorship of Drs. James Sherman and Jan Sheldon. He has more than eight years of experience working with children, adolescents, and adults with autism and other developmental disabilities. Justin began his career working for Drs. Taubman, Leaf, and McEachin at Autism Partnership, both as a behavior therapist and as a research coordinator. His research has included looking at ways to improve social skills for children with autism, developing friendships, and comparing different teaching methods. While at the University of Kansas, Dr. Leaf was the Co-Director of The Social Skills Group. He has published articles in professional journals and has presented at national and state conferences and invited events.

Karen McKinnon, M. Ed. Psych., MAPS

Karen McKinnon is a registered psychologist, with a master's degree in educational psychology. She is the Site Director of Autism Partnership in Australia and has worked in the field of applied behavior analysis since 1995. She completed an internship with Autism Partnership in the United States, as a way to develop her clinical skills and provide a higher quality of service to families in Australia. Ms. McKinnon has consulted both nationally and internationally to families of children with autism. Her work includes diagnostic assessments, psychological consultation, school consultation, and supervision of both home- and school-based behavioral intervention programs, along with Autism Partnership staff training and professional development. She regularly presents papers at seminars and conferences on a range of topics relating to the application of applied behavior analysis to children with an autism spectrum disorder.

Tracee Parker, Ph.D.

Tracee Parker has more than 25 years of treatment and research experience in the field of autism and developmental disabilities and earned a doctoral degree in psychology from the University of California at Los Angeles (UCLA) in 1990. Her training experience included five years working on the UCLA Young Autism Project directed by Dr. Ivar Lovaas. During this time, she served in the capacities of teaching and research assistant as well as Clinic Supervisor. As a research assistant, Dr. Parker was closely involved in a number of studies including the long-term treatment follow-up of young autistic children and changes in self-stimulatory behavior during treatment. Dr. Parker worked 12 years at Straight Talk Clinic, a residential and day behavioral treatment program serving adults with developmental disabilities; she served as Associate Director at this organization until 1997. Dr. Parker is currently a Clinical Associate with Autism Partnership and Associate Director for Behavior Therapy and Learning Center. She has presented at national and international conferences in the areas of behavioral treatment, autism and social/sexual issues, and intervention. Over the past 20 years, she has provided consultation to residential and day programs, school districts, families, and other related agencies.

Julia Peacock, M.S.

Julia Peacock began implementing intensive applied behavior analysis programs in California in 1995 and joined Autism Partnership UK when it was launched in 2000. She earned a bachelor's degree in psychology and social behavior from the University of California, Irvine. She received her master's degree in applied behavior analysis from St. Cloud State University, Minnesota, in 2006 and is a Board-Certified Behavior Analyst (BCBA). Ms. Peacock became the Site Director of the U.K. organization in 2005, becoming responsible for clinical supervision, program development, and staff training across the country. She has presented to international audiences and has consulted to families and schools in the United Kingdom and countries throughout Europe and Asia. Currently, she provides consultation and training to families in the United States.

Jon Rafuse, M.A.

Jon Rafuse graduated from the University of California at Los Angeles (UCLA) in 1988 with a bachelor's degree in psychology and then went on to receive a master's degree in clinical psychology from Antioch University in 1991. In 1992, he began working for the May Institute in Chatham, Massachusetts, eventually running one of the off-campus group homes housing students dramatically impaired with autism spectrum disorder. In 1995, he joined the Autism Partnership staff, providing intensive applied behavior analysis services to the families of children diagnosed with autism. His experience in this specific area of behavioral psychology spans 15 years. Currently, Mr. Rafuse is a consultant providing advanced training, mentoring, and supervision to service providers and teachers within school districts across the United States. He has presented both nationally and internationally at conferences on applied behavior analysis, and has consulted and trained families, program staff and school districts throughout the United States, England, Saudi Arabia, Australia, and New Zealand.

Julide Saltuklaroglu

Julide Saltuklaroglu serves as the Site Director of the Autism Partnership Calgary office. She has been supervising, directing, and implementing applied behavior analysis (ABA) programs for children and adolescents diagnosed with ASD since 1993. Her background includes working as a research assistant in the field, providing program supervision and consultation for families and schools throughout western Canada, and filling an extensive role as the on-site Behavior Consultant for an ABA model classroom for adolescents with ASD in Maui, Hawaii. Ms. Saltuklaroglu is also the President and Behavior Consultant for Behaviour Therapy and Learning Centre, a Calgary-based PUF preschool education program for children with special needs.

Andrea Waks, J.D., M.A.

Andrea Waks is the Director of Client Services at Autism Partnership. She began working with children with autism in the late 1970s at the University of California at Los Angeles (UCLA) on the Young Autism Project, where she served as a Senior Therapist, Research Assistant, and Teaching Assistant. Ms. Waks has worked with Drs. Leaf, McEachin, and Taubman on the Young Autism Project, the Behavior Therapy and Learning Center, Straight Talk, and Autism Partnership. She earned her master's degree in general psychology at Pepperdine University in 1983 and returned to school in 1993 to pursue a law degree. She practiced special education law, representing families of children with autism, before returning to Autism Partnership on a full-time basis. Her current duties include conducting behavioral assessments, individual education plan (IEP) preparation, policy review, and classroom consultations. She consults with families and school districts both locally and nationally.

Introduction

For a person to receive a diagnosis of autism spectrum disorder (ASD), there must be deficits in communication and social skills as well as the presence of patterns of repetitive and stereotyped behaviors. Historically, however, the emphasis in treatment and research has been on communication. Programming efforts have focused on helping children learn to understand language and to speak. It is our firm belief that, although communication is important, social skills are also a core deficit in ASD. These deficiencies result in reduced social opportunities and often lead to loneliness, isolation, and depression for persons with ASD. Social skills problems simply reduce the quality of life. Yet intervention, programming, teaching, and research focused on social skills and their development tend to lag well behind treatment efforts in other skill domains. A literature search of applied behavior analysis (ABA) research in autism will reveal this to be so. The difference in the number of studies done on social skills versus, say, communication, is staggering. But why?

One possible answer to this question reflects the nature of the social skills phenomenon. Communication, while complex, seems to lend itself more easily to conceptualization, task analysis, programming, and ultimately intervention. Social skills are harder to get your head and therapeutic hand around. They consist of many, many components knitted together. These skill components are difficult to understand both individually and as parts of the whole. In a sense, they are analogous to smoke—intangible though visible, filling a room but seemingly impossible to grasp and fully contain.

Not only are these skills multifaceted and subtle, but each individual involved in social interactions also brings a distinct presence to those interactions. This is true whether the interaction is a simple nodded "hello" when passing on the street or the intricate dance of a first date. Thus teaching social skills can be daunting—much like attempting to restore a shattered water glass. The rebuilding task may involve hundreds or thousands of pieces fitting together in an elaborate pattern; it may take a great deal of time and patient effort; and in the end, it may look like a water glass again, but may not effectively hold water. Teaching the pieces of a complex social competency while planning for the most appropriate application of that skill is a balancing act. The teaching mandates a great deal of practice and teacher expertise, but it is certainly worth the effort.

This book represents an effort to lend some assistance to work in this challenging area. Based on the decades of research and interventional experiences of the authors, it provides information and content that will assist treatment and education practitioners, as well as families, in addressing the social skills needs of all persons on the autism spectrum. In this book, we attempt to fill what is generally a great void in an especially critical programming area for persons with ASD.

The book provides information on important issues relating to social skills and persons with ASD (e.g., Chapters 1, 4, and 5), ways to assess competencies and develop programs (e.g., Chapters 6 and 7), social skills curricula and instructional content (e.g., Chapter 8 and the Curriculum section), and methods and means for teaching and programming in the social skills area (e.g., Chapters 2, 3, 4, and 5).

The contemporary ABA approach to social skills education and treatment contained within this book is designed to focus on building more than simple social responses. This ABA approach is intended to capture the essence of authentic social competence and genuine relationship development while remaining systematic and analytic.

Hence, the methodology and content of the book are directed at establishing true social skills development, so that an individual with ASD, and those around him or her, are not forced to count on mere hope and magic for social growth. The book embodies a comprehensive push to give work on social skills for individuals with ASD its due. It is designed to travel far beyond the rote, simplistic, naïve, or undefined and truly help persons with ASD develop real social competencies as well as genuine, meaningful, and life-enriching relationships.

We invite you to join us on this exciting journey. Social skills development is an area of great novelty, variability, uniqueness, and challenge. For interventionists, therapists, researchers, teachers, and family members alike, it is critical to finally prioritize this vast learning domain and not falter in addressing it, because ultimately, social skills are much of what makes us, us.

Mitchell Taubman

Ronald Leaf

John McEachin

1

Why Play and Social Skills?

Ronald Leaf and Mitchell Taubman

Play and social skills are perhaps the most critical skills that a child can learn. Learning these skills is important for a number of reasons. First, plain and simple, these skills strongly influence the quality of life. When all is said and done, it doesn't matter how smart a person is or how many facts he or she knows; rather, what is most critical is whether the individual has at least one meaningful friendship. Is there someone the person spends time with, can talk to, and enjoy life with? When people don't have meaningful friendships, passions, and hobbies, that emptiness all too often results in boredom, isolation, and eventually depression. Tragically, in the world of autism spectrum disorder (ASD), play and social skills are all too often not a priority. Home programs generally concentrate on developing language, and schools focus on academic skills. Although these skills can certainly be helpful to children, they pale in comparison to the importance of social and play skills.

Being able to play with other children in a meaningful way will only increase the happiness of children with ASD as well as provide them with situations in which to develop language and communication skills as well as cognitive abilities, including abstract processing.

Facilitation of Language

Experience shows that children's language often improves dramatically through being around peers. Obviously, more than simple exposure is involved in this phenomenon. Simply placing children in general education or just exposing them to family friends will not help them develop necessary skills and, ultimeately, lead to friendships. Rather, this effort requires systematic programming designed to reduce interfering behaviors, increase interests in peers, and teach children how to observe, model, and respond to their peers. Once this foundation has been laid, then children can receive tremendous benefits from structured social opportunities.

We usually see far more natural development of language through play and social than through structured therapy. Although structured therapy may get the process started, it is generally through play and social interactions where the most dramatic progress occurs. Children are far more receptive to vocalizing and speaking when they are relaxed and having fun. Typically, children are far more vocal when they are playing on the computer or in the pool than when they are in a one-on-one teaching situation. In fact, structured therapy may sometimes actually inhibit language.

Language is developed far more naturally through social effort. Children learn from other children how to speak naturally and in a childlike manner. Adults teaching language to children often produce adult-sounding language. For example, when a child is asked, "How old are you?" an adult often teaches a child to respond, "I am four years old" or "Four years old." Although this is a polite answer, it is far too formal and not how children typically respond. Three-year-old children do not even give a verbal answer—they simply hold up three fingers. Four-year-olds will hold up four fingers and say, "Four." Older children answer this question by simply giving the number (i.e., "Five," "Ten"). Age-inappropriate child responses make the child sound unnatural and can sometimes complicate the integration process. Peers use natural ("cool") language, whereas adults naturally speak as adults. Even when they try to act as peers, it is not natural.

Incidental Learning

One of the fundamental obstacles in autism is the extreme difficulty individuals have in learning through casual observation. Providing social and play opportunities as well as skill development will greatly assist a child in learning how to acquire information through everyday casual experiences. Whereas the majority of the information typically developing children learn is gathered in an off-handed manner and often through observation and watching others, children with ASD generally require direct teaching. Therefore, one of the most important goals of therapy is teaching children how to learn from others. Many programs are devoted to developing these specific skills (e.g., joint attention, group nonverbal imitation, observational learning curriculum).[65]

Social and play interactions become a primary means for a child to learn a variety of skills and acquire vast knowledge. Naturally, for this learning to occur, careful and systematic intervention is required (see Chapters 2 and 8 and the Curriculum section of this book). However, the benefits are that a child will learn in the most natural manner.

Children with ASD often respond far more favorably under highly structured conditions, thereby increasing everyone's reluctance to work under less structured conditions. However, if this issue is not addressed quickly, the problem merely becomes worse and continues to greatly impede progress. It is essential that persons with ASD master how to learn in less structured and more natural settings as soon as possible. It is through this process that integration and generalization become more likely to occur.

Social Reinforcement

Perhaps one of the biggest benefits of socials skills training is that the peers become an important influence on children, sometimes having a far more powerful effect than adults. We have often found that peers can stop inappropriate behaviors faster, more effectively, and much more naturally than teachers. Additionally, their consequences are far more typical. Whereas adults sometimes sound very therapeutic (e.g., "Use your words," "You're not being a good friend," "Are you feeling angry?"), children tend to be far more direct, politically incorrect, natural, and effective (e.g., "Don't do that!", "Give it to me!", "That's weird!"). Their actions can also be quite effective and natural, such as taking a toy back.

With time, children with ASD may develop a desire to please their peers. This is a crucial hurdle in the intervention process. Peers will come to be natural supports for appropriate behaviors. Consequently, generalization is far more likely to occur. Adult monitoring, therefore, becomes less necessary. We have found integration substantially more successful when peers are important.

Resistance to Teaching Social and Play Skills

We often find tremendous resistance to making social and play skills a priority in home and school programs. Frequently heard comments include:

"I am more concerned right now with getting him to speak."

"Once he has language, then we can work on social skills."

"I don't want to take any time away from speech and academics."

"My other children don't have lots of friends, so why should my child with ASD?"

Professionals and parents may similarly feel that language or academics are priorities, or that social behavior will simply develop on its own or through social exposure.

There are arguments to counter all of these positions. As discussed earlier, social and play effort can greatly enhance language development. Further, as a student grows, academic instruction becomes increasingly a social matter. Not only do students work with one another in groups, but social elements (e.g., emphasis cues, gestures that indicate exaggeration) increasingly become an integral part of lectures and discussions. Additionally, although a child may not be inclined to be highly social, learning to navigate the complex and challenging social world eventually becomes a necessary reality. Finally, although not all people are social, most everyone learns from observing social interactions. Therefore, it is essential that a child learns this way as well! In terms of priority in the education and treatment of children with ASD, we see development of social skills as paramount.

Resistance may sometimes reflect just how difficult it is to generate curriculum for these behaviors (see Chapter 7 on developing curriculum). Unlike language and academic skills, for which you can develop a structured curriculum fairly easily, teaching play and social skills requires far more flexibility and creativity.

The specific play and social skills you teach will largely be based on the skills and social culture of the target group of peers. Therefore, prepackaged social or play programs are often of less use with children with ASD. For example, the toys peers commonly play with will differ not only in regard to age and gender but will also depend on where you live. Naturally, what children play with in India differs widely from what they play with in the United States. Likewise, what children play with (and how they play with those items) in Boston can be quite different than what they play with in Dallas. Even areas of a particular city may differ in terms of the types of toys children use and the games they play. Therefore, developing a specific and exhaustive list of toys and play activities would be difficult.

Similar to toy play, social behaviors differ widely—probably more widely than play choices. As a simple example, how children initiate peer interaction varies greatly. Whereas most adults teach children to approach and say, "Do you want to play with me?", real-world interactions rarely begin this way among most young typically developing children. In some areas, children simply hover or play next to another child. Sometimes children simply grab another child to facilitate social interaction. In some situations, children may simply make a comment as an initiation (e.g., "What are you playing with?"). No one way is any better than the others; they are just different. Further, the range of possible social and play needs can seem nearly infinite. Thus it is often necessary to develop highly sophisticated programs that are individually, situationally, and culturally appropriate—a discouraging proposition.

Not only are social and play programs difficult to develop and apply, but because of the uniquely individual and often short-lived nature of such behaviors, they are difficult to teach. It may be hard to instruct in such areas, or a parent or professional may feel that that he or she is greatly altering (to the point of artificiality or unrecognizability) the social or play ability in an effort to teach it. Therefore, family members and teachers often fall back to their comfort zone— namely, teaching more defined and structured skills. Application of instructional techniques to social and play instruction can be a complicated matter as well. For example, although Discrete Trail Teaching techniques can be used when teaching these skills, they require far more flexibility in their implementation. One must be more subtle in prompting and providing consequences, for example. Additionally, it is extremely beneficial if teachers possess great play and social skills (and style) themselves. Having a natural and fluid teaching manner can be critical. This isn't always an easy matter.

Another source of resistance is the impact of social and play work on behavior. Often behavioral problems become much more evident in the less structured arrangement of play and social skills instruction. Naturally, this is not a good reason to avoid teaching these skills. In fact, it is exactly the reason to work on it. It is critical to address behavior problems in all situations! Even so, this complication can generate avoidance.

A further reason cited for postponing teaching these skills is the notion that children need language for social skills. Undoubtedly, language is helpful—but it is not essential. All one has to do is go to a park where children from different cultures are playing. You will quickly see that they are able to play beautifully even though they do not speak the same language. Toddlers with limited language are social with peers. Even while engaging in parallel play, they can be observed truly referencing and interacting with one another and adjusting their own play based on the play behavior of others. Additionally, getting them ready for the social experience may take a while and does not require language in the beginning.

Although many forces present obstacles to social and play programming, the importance of such work remains clear. Effort in these areas may be deprioritized or avoided entirely, albeit rarely because of the relative value of such efforts. Social and play deficits are core to the challenges of ASD. Interventional and educational efforts in these areas are correspondingly central and essential. There is no denying that such work is difficult. However, the remaining chapters of this book are designed to reduce some of the burden and facilitate these important efforts.

2

Teaching Interactions

Mitchell Taubman, Justin Leaf, and Alyne Kuyumjian

For people with autism spectrum disorder (ASD), social skills just don't develop on their own or even easily. They need to be taught. To teach social skills, like the ones provided in the Curriculum section in this book, a solid teaching method must be used. Today, a range of such methods are being used to teach social skills—from those with strong research support (e.g., video modeling,[21] pivotal response training,[56] and discrete trial teaching[65]) to those with some empirical support (e.g., social stories[1]) to those interventions with little to no empirical support (e.g., floor time, relationship development intervention, and music therapy). One teaching approach that has been used with children and adolescents with ASD with great success for many years, and that has a growing body of research support, is the Teaching Interaction (TI) procedure.[26, 58, 61, 63] Teaching Interactions, combined with Discrete Trial Training,[65] can be a very effective way to teach numerous social skills (like many of the ones in the curriculum) at home, at school, in the community, and in teaching settings ranging from one-on-one instruction to large groups.

Modeling, practice, and feedback have been used for many years in applied behavior analysis (ABA) to build a variety of skills and behaviors.[12, 14, 15, 96] The TI procedure expands on this basic approach, providing for a systematic and interactive type of instruction that consists of six steps.

What follows is a brief sketch of the TI method (a more complete description is provided later in this chapter). The first step of the teaching interaction procedure is to **label and identify** the social skill that is being targeted. In the second step, the teacher provides a meaningful **rationale,** or reason why the learner should engage in the social behavior. In the third step, the teacher first **describe**s the behavior by breaking the targeted skill into smaller behavioral parts, and then **demonstrates** the desired behavior. In the fourth step, the learner has the opportunity to **practice** or role-play the desired social behavior with the teacher. In the fifth step of the TI, the teacher provides specific **feedback** based on the learner's practice of the skill during role-plays. In the sixth and final step, the learner is provided with an **external consequence** or reinforcement (e.g., points on a token system) based on his or her performance of the skill as well as the overall level and quality of his or her "learning how to learn" behaviors (e.g., compliance, attention, engaged effort) during the TI process.

Steps of the Teaching Interaction

1 Label and Identify

2 Rationale

3 Description and Demonstration

4 Practice

5 Feedback

6 Optional External Consequence

Let's look at a brief example of a Teaching Interaction:

TEACHER: Hey, Todd.

TODD: Hi, Mr. Kaufman.

TEACHER: I noticed that you had a little trouble when Tony was sitting next to you and tried to help you with your math.

TODD: Yeah, I didn't want to look stupid.

TEACHER: Well, sometimes it's hard to *accept help* **[Label and Identify]**. But taking help from someone can be a good thing. Know why?

TODD: Uh, no.

TEACHER: Because it's a way to learn new things, to get better at things. I do it all the time. Smart people do it all the time too—that's how they get smart. And you know, bosses get their workers to help them all the time, too. **[Rationales]**

TODD: Oh, yeah. You know I want to be a boss. Um, what do I do?

TEACHER: Well if you are going to *accept help,* the first part is, right after people ask if they can help, you turn toward them, look at them, and with a smile on your face make a statement showing that you welcome and appreciate their help—something like, "Would you? Thanks" or "Thanks, I could use some help." Why don't you be Tony and I'll be you, and I'll show you what I mean. **[Demonstration and Description]**

TEACHER: Did that make some sense? Why don't you give it a try? But this time you can be you! **[Practice]**

After role-play, the teacher continues:

TEACHER: That was terrific. You were very smooth; you seemed to really want the help and were appreciative, too. And you showed that with what you said and how you said it, especially with that big ole' smile on your face. But there was one thing you forgot. Can you think of it? **[Feedback]**

TODD: I forgot to look at you?

TEACHER: Yup. Let's try it again. Do it just like last time, except look at me when you make your statement, like this: **[Redemonstrate and then Repractice]**

After the second practice, the teacher continues:

TEACHER: That was perfect! As soon as I offered help, you turned toward me, looked at me [teacher gives high five], smiled, and made a statement that told me you wanted the help and even appreciated my offer. Just beautiful! **[Feedback]** Give yourself 10 bonus points. **[Optional External Consequence]** There are some other things for us to practice, too, but I have to tell you, I think you'll be ready next time you need some math help and Tony, or anyone else, offers it to you. Thanks, bud. You did great!

Both in the research literature and throughout decades of clinical practice, the TI method has been found to be a very effective way to teach a variety of social and nonsocial behaviors for children and adolescents with ASD. Let's look at the history and research that supports the TI. (Note: If you are mainly interested in the TI procedure itself, skip ahead to the section entitled "Teaching Interactions Are Not for Everyone." You can always return to the following section if interested in the story and empirical support behind the Teaching Interaction procedure.)

The History and Research Behind the Teaching Interaction

The Teaching Interaction procedure was first developed as a part of the Teaching Family Model—an ABA program developed to treat delinquent youth.[93, 94] Initially, research on the Teaching Interaction, as part of the Teaching Family Model, examined the effectiveness of the procedure with populations other than persons with ASD.[15, 72, 80, 96]

In an early study, Minkin and colleagues[80] implemented the TI procedure to increase the conversation skills of four girls ranging from 12 to 14 years of age. The four girls in this study were identified as having difficulty communicating appropriately with both peers and adults. This study examined whether use of the TI procedure would increase the four girls' ability to use conversational questions and provide positive conversational feedback within a four-minute discussion with an unknown adult. Results of the study showed that all four participants were able to increase both their ability to ask questions and to give appropriate feedback following intervention. Maloney and colleagues[72] replicated these findings, but also showed that four girls between the ages of 13 and 15 were able to appropriately communicate with adults once a TI procedure was implemented.

Research on and use of the Teaching Interaction led to its inclusion in two manuals describing treatment procedures for populations other individuals with ASD. The first manual, *The ASSET Manual*,[48] is a guidebook that clinicians can use to implement the TI procedure to teach skills that include conversation, resisting peer pressure, following instructions, and problem solving. The second manual, *Effective Skills for Child-Care Workers: A Training Manual from Boys Town*,[27] shows how the TI procedure can be used to teach a variety of skills, such as initiating conversations, giving compliments, sharing, and turn taking.

Although no research was published on the effectiveness of the TI procedure for children or adolescents with ASD until 2009,[64] it was brought from the University of Kansas's Teaching Family Program to the UCLA Young Autism Project[69] and autism treatment by the lead author of this chapter in 1980. Research on training staff treatment methods that actually included Teaching Interactions was published after that time.[112] Additionally, research on its use with children with ASD had also been presented at many professional conferences.[63, 67, 90, 91, 113] Thus Teaching Interactions have been successfully used within ASD treatment for several decades.

In 2009, Justin Leaf and colleagues examined the TI procedure as a means to teach prosocial skills to three young children diagnosed[64] with ASD. In this study, the authors examined whether the TI procedure could teach social skills across four domains: social communication (e.g., appropriate initiations), play (e.g., following a peer), emotion skills (e.g., providing compliments), and friendship identification (e.g., choosing the same person throughout the day). The TI procedure in this study was implemented in a one-on-one setting and was used in conjunction with a token economy and priming. Prior to intervention, all three participants displayed near-zero levels of the target social skills; following intervention, significant increases were seen across all skills and across all participants.

Five follow-up studies have since been conducted to further determine the effectiveness of the TI procedure. Justin Leaf and associates[62] examined this procedure in a group setting for five children diagnosed along the autism spectrum. In this study, the TI method was used to teach participants how to change the game when someone was bored, to show appreciation, to provide compliments, and to make empathetic statements. Results of the study showed that all participants were able to learn the skills taught to them. In addition, participants were able to generalize skills to more natural environments 85% of the time, either with or without reinforcement being provided.

Dotson, Leaf, Sheldon, and Sherman[26] also examined the effects of the TI procedure implemented in a group setting for four adolescents diagnosed with autistic disorder. In this study, participants were able to learn various aspects of conversational skills in both structured and unstructured settings.

Oppenheim, Leaf, Call, Sheldon, and Sherman[88] examined the effectiveness of the TI procedure in teaching two children diagnosed with ASD how to play Uno, Yahtzee Junior, and Go Fish. Results of this study suggest that participants were able to effectively play each of the three games following implementation of the procedure.

A study by Kuyumjian and colleagues[58] assessed the effectiveness of the TI method in teaching social skills (sportsmanship, response to contemporary greetings, responding to peers' social initiations, and expanding social conversations) to four children with ASD. These researchers also suggested a protocol for generalizing the learned skills to independent use in naturally occurring social situations. Prior to receiving the intervention, participants displayed their designated target behaviors at either low or extremely variable levels. Following the implementation of the TI procedure, all participants performed their skills at high and consistent levels. In addition, this study used a systematic generalization strategy, which effectively showed transfer to natural, everyday situations. Results of this study demonstrated that Teaching Interactions were highly effective both during instruction and in follow-up probes.

In the most recent study, Justin Leaf, Oppenheim, Call, Sheldon, Sherman, and Taubman[88] compared the Teaching Interaction procedure to Social Stories. Six children between the ages of 4 and 13, all of whom were diagnosed along the autism spectrum, were evaluated on various social skills in both structured and naturalistic settings. Both Teaching Interactions and Social Stories were implemented in a one-on-one setting. The researchers determined that all of the children were able to learn all the social skills taught to them when the TI procedure was used, whereas only a few of the participants were able to learn a few skills when taught by Social Stories. Additionally, the children demonstrated far better generalization of the skills taught with Teaching Interactions to natural environments than the skills taught with Social Stories. Finally, the results showed that the TI procedure was more efficient both in terms of number of sessions and actual time necessary for children to learn the various social skills. Thus the TI procedure may be a superior way to teach social skills to children and adolescents with ASD as compared to Social Stories.

A growing body of research supports the contention that Teaching Interactions are an effective way to teach social skills to both children and adolescents diagnosed with ASD. Although appropriate for teaching a variety of skills, the TI procedure is an especially useful and effective instructional method for teaching social skills to children diagnosed with ASD.

Teaching Interactions Are Not for Everyone

As the name implies, Teaching Interactions involve social as well as communication interchanges between the teacher and learner. Therefore, a child must have certain prerequisites to participate in meaningful TIs. If these prerequisites are not present, then using Discrete Trial Teaching[65] would be a more appropriate and effective means for teaching social skills.

First, a child needs to have at least basic conversational ability (both expressive and receptive) to be able to participate in a Teaching Interaction. He or she must be able to understand basic descriptions of behavior, detailed feedback, and at least simple discussions of reasons. The child must also be able to answer basic questions about what is being taught and engage in some of the conversation that is core to the "interactional" nature of this teaching approach. Likewise, the learner must at minimum show social tolerance, awareness of others, and basic social responsivity to (by definition) be a participant in the instructional interaction (after all, it is not called a "teaching monologue"). Finally, the student must be able to understand at least the basic forms of such concepts as cause and effect, anticipation of events, and the relationship between practice and later use of skills.

> ## Prerequisites for Teaching Interactions
>
> - Conversational Abilities
> - Social Abilities
> - Cognitive Abilities

The Teaching Interaction Procedure

The TI procedure has many steps, which can be implemented in structured or unstructured, planned or unplanned, and individual or group teaching situations. Regardless of the arrangement or format, the Teaching Interaction should consist of the five (and in many cases six) major components. Let's look at each of these steps in detail.

Label and Identification

The first component of the TI procedure is the labeling and identification of the target behavior. Identification and labeling of a skill involve pointing out what is being taught and giving it a name. Frequently, this step also includes letting the student know times and places the skill could be used.

The purpose of this step is to make sure that the learner clearly understands which skill is being taught. Further, having a clear name for the skill can help when priming is used (e.g., before entering a room, "Now remember how well you did when we practiced *greeting a group of people*") and makes for clear feedback (e.g., "You did such a great job of *asking for help* just now. You made it look easy!").

Several features characterize a good label. Most importantly, the label should be clear. It should capture the skill being taught and do so in as few words as possible. Also, it should be made up of language that fits the age level and peer culture of the learner (e.g., "Handling it when you are told what to do" versus "Adequately coping when receiving overwhelming instructions from adults").

When identifying the behavior, it is good practice to define what the behavior *is* and what it *is not*. Further, such identification should clearly indicate where and when the skill is relevant or an issue. Identification should relate the skill to the student's past history and personal experience. Past or present occurrences or issues in the child's life that point to the area of need should be included here (e.g., "Remember when your classmate asked you a question? Well, we want to work on what to do when that happens.").

Label and Identification
• Clear and encompassing
• Age and culture appropriate
• Focused on what, when, and where
• Related to personal history

Rationales

The second, and certainly critical, component of the TI procedure is the giving of a *meaningful* rationale. A rationale is not just a reason to engage in the behavior, but rather the naturally occurring, fundamental, and meaningful-to-the-learner purpose for engaging in the behavior. When we mention the natural consequences of a behavior, such as when we talk about trying to fade from artificial reinforcers (e.g., tokens) to natural, maintaining consequences (natural outcomes), we are referring to the stuff of rationales. A good rationale usually takes the form of an *if/then* statement (e.g., "*If* you share with your friends, *then* your friends might let you play with their cool dinosaur toys"). In short, a good rationale includes naturalistic and realistic outcomes and meets the learner's personal needs and desires. This can be the first step in connecting the learner to the natural consequences that will eventually maintain the behavior. This connection will happen once the learner is good enough at the skill to actually achieve those outcomes. A reason like "You will get points on your token system" may motivate the child in the moment (much like a bribe) and describe an actual outcome. It does not make for a good rationale, however, because it does not connect to the natural consequences that will assume control as the artificial reasons (tokens) are faded.

With rationales, learners are more likely to accept instruction. Further, they begin to develop an internal locus of control; that is, they recognize that they have influence over the outcomes they experience. Good rationales help the learner anticipate outcomes and develop a sense of cause and effect. With time and some teaching, some students even begin to develop meaningful rationales themselves.

In addition to providing natural outcomes, rationales need to be meaningful to the learner. Canned or stock rationales just don't motivate students or make them invested in the teaching or skill acquisition. Neither do those rationales that are based on reasons important to the teacher but not the learner, or those rationales that provide reasons that just do not make sense to the particular learner. For example, for a student who insists on arguing with peers to "educate" them as to the "right" opinion, learning to *discuss and suggest* may be a targeted skill. The rationale "Kids will not want to play with you if you argue" may not be meaningful to a child who really doesn't want to play with others; for that child, other children are important only when they have an opinion that needs changing. A better rationale in such a case might be, "If you *discuss and suggest* rather than argue, kids will be more likely to change their opinions."

Rationales
• Natural outcomes
• Meaningful to learner

A good rationale clearly describes to the learner natural occurring reasons why the person should engage in the social behavior that speaks to him or her as an individual. Meaningful rationales are rationales that will motivate the learner to engage in the proper behavior. Prior to beginning a Teaching Interaction, the teacher should prepare by coming up with reasons why the student would want to engage in the behavior. If a reason to engage in the behavior is not important to the learner, then it should not be used. Furthermore, if the teacher is having great difficulty with generating a rationale, perhaps there are none—and the skill, not being in the student's interest, should not be taught.

Multiple rationales may be used for a particular skill. At the same time, going on and on about the numerous reasons for learning a skill during a single teaching session may not help the learning process.

Rationales can include the advantages offered by the new skill, the advantage of not doing things the "old way," the disadvantage of the "old way," and the disadvantage of not using the new skill. During the first few teaching sessions, the teacher would develop these rationales. Over time, the teacher might come up with some rationales and have the learner suggest additional ones. When a skill is taught across many sessions (which can often be the case), it is certainly not necessary to restate the rationale every time.

We have found it beneficial at times to demonstrate rationales in action. These "living rationales" may consist of demonstrations performed for the student. They can also be part of the discrimination training periodically included in the TI process (discussed later in this chapter). Living rationales may also involve the teacher pointing out instances in the student's natural environment when the target skill is performed by others and positive outcomes result (e.g., "Did you see that when Bobby waited to interrupt, the others really listened to what he had to say?"). Living rationales often help the learner understand and accept the rationale, by making it clear and real.

Description/Demonstration

The third step of the TI procedure is the teacher's description/demonstration. In this component, the teacher describes and demonstrates the skill (or part of the skill). Usually, only part of a skill is taught in a single TI session. Thus segments are taught in individual sessions and then chained together over time. A segment may be a step in a task analysis (see Chapter 7) or a phase within an already established social skills curriculum (see the Curriculum section of this book). However, it is very likely that adjustments will have to be made in the size of the step or lesson once the TI begins. It is not uncommon to bite off more than the student can chew, or to start too simply.

The teacher should describe the segment being taught, including all necessary elements. This information might include not only what is being said, but also how it is being said—that is, facial expressions, voice tone, gaze, and body language. It may include visible actions, supportive elements (e.g., use of stress management tools such as taking deep breaths), and internal, cognitive parts (e.g., self-talk or instructions). Descriptions should be detailed and clear, and should convey discrete behaviors. They should also contain understandable (at the learner's level), student-friendly language.

As an example of a relatively simple social skill, in the study by Kuyumjian et al.[58] the components of good sportsmanship were described as follows:

> When you win a game against someone else, the first thing you want to do is say something, really briefly, about winning but do it in a cool manner. For example, say something like "Yes" or "I win" with an excited or happy voice tone, but not too loud, and do it only one time. After that, say something to the other person that will make them feel better about losing, like "Good game" or "Nice try." You want to say that to them with a voice tone that is supportive and kind, and not sarcastic or rude. Also, when you make that statement, have a neutral facial expression neither happy nor sad, and make sure to face the other person.
>
> Next, suggest a rematch. If the other person wants to, then play again. If not, ask the other person what they may want to play instead. If the person does not want to continue playing with you, say something to let them know that you heard them and that what they said was okay, and to end the time you have spent with them. For example, you could say something like, "Okay, see you later."

It would be very unlikely that, in one teaching session, the teacher would provide the entire description presented here. It would make the session very hard to run and would certainly overwhelm the learner. Rather, the teacher might, in one teaching session, describe only the first step.

In the demonstration portion, the teacher models for the learner all of the components described within that teaching session. Modeling provides an exact demonstration of the behavior, or component, to be learned. Demonstrations are usually in vivo (happening live), but can be written or pictorial (as in Social Stories[1]) or consist of video modeling.[68, 86, 110] Further or repeated descriptions may accompany the demonstration as a narration of sorts.

In addition to demonstrating the new way to respond (the new skill), the teacher may demonstrate the old way the student responded. This can be tricky, however (think how pleasant it is to watch a video of your horrible golf swing), and might instead involve the modeling of an inappropriate version of the skill different from the student's version. Often, the learner with ASD cannot differentiate the inappropriate versus appropriate version of the skill or its components. This is where discrimination training (discussed later) would come into play—occurring either before, during, or after the description/demonstration portion of the TI procedure. Discrimination training involves having the student discriminate between the correct and incorrect performance of the behavior by someone else, before having the student practice the skill himself or herself. It ensures understanding of the skill being taught.

Description/Demonstration
• Thorough description of the skill or learnable component
• Description can include what is said, how it is said, and which facial expressions and body language are appropriate
• Description can include external action and internal (e.g., cognitive) elements
• Modeling can be in vivo, pictorial, or video
• Discrimination training may be included

On some occasions—for example, when the skill has been described numerous times in prior Teaching Interactions, the description/demonstration step can be excluded. Additionally, if the skill has not been modeled before but the teacher believes that the student could perform the skill appropriately on his or her own (or believes that attempting to do so would be a good exercise for the student), then the TI may not include a description or demonstration and instead will go directly to the practice step.

Once the skill or its segment has been sufficiently described and modeled for the student, it is the student's turn to perform the targeted skill.

Practice

Perhaps the most important component of the TI procedure is the practice or role-play portion. All too often, we have seen teaching that involves just labeling of the skill, perhaps a rationale, a description of the skill, and maybe a demonstration. Such teaching ends with the expectation that somehow the student will now be able to perform the complex skill being discussed. Can a student driver learn to operate a manual transmission on a car just by learning why it is important to do so and by watching others do it? Is watching Tiger Woods play golf on TV all you need to do before buying clubs and entering a tournament? Can you make your first ever presentation to the board of directors without some rehearsal? Where and when in life are modeling and discussion sufficient for complex skill development? This is true with any population, let alone with challenged learners.

It is critical to learning to make sure that the student has sufficient opportunity to practice the skill and that practice continues until the skill is mastered. What is practiced follows the description/demonstration. That is, students should fully practice what (usually the segment of the skill) has been modeled (including not just what is said or done, but how it is said or done). They should not be expected—and certainly not be required—to practice more than they have been shown. If a student competently exceeds what has been described and demonstrated, that is typically fine and should be allowed. This outcome usually indicates that what was described and demonstrated was too simple or limited. The TI can later return to the description/demonstration step and greater complexity can be added for further practice. If the student struggles with the practice, then it could signify that too much has been attempted. In such a case, the teacher can interrupt that practice and return to a simplified or reduced description and demonstration.

Within the practice, the student role-plays the skill (or, more likely, the portion of the skill) being taught, with the teacher as partner, in a simulation. The teacher should design this step of the teaching interaction in a way that will increase the chance that the student's practice will be successful. Therefore, the practice is most often initially removed from natural circumstances (hence it is role-play) and set up in a way that will minimize the obstacles to successful performance. For example, the practice may initially occur with adults rather than with targeted peers, in a setting removed from challenging circumstances, at a time when emotions are not high, and, as noted previously, involving only learning components that the student can successfully manage. The teacher has control over the form and extent of the practice through setup and planning and by how he or she plays the other party in the role-play. In this way, statements, styles, complexity, challenges, and other factors can be adjusted either up or down.

The component that is being taught is practiced until mastery is achieved, whether that requires several practices within a teaching session or practice across numerous sessions. Several factors may affect the teacher's decision about the number of practices, including momentum, student fatigue, and time constraints and other logistical issues.

Practice

- Practice is essential for learning.
- Practice what is described/demonstrated.
- Initially practice the skill in contrived role-play.
- Arrange role-play to ensure student success.
- With mastery, what is practiced expands over time.

With any Teaching Interaction, what is being practiced will be systematically expanded over time with successful acquisition on the part of the student. In turn, the expansion of the skill, heightened complexity, and increased independence of performance will first be reflected in the description/demonstration portion of the TI. The expectation in practice should always follow what is presented in the description/demonstration segment. In time (see the discussion of generalization later in this chapter), effort is also directed at working the fully learned skill into application in the natural environment.

Feedback

Numerous studies have shown the importance of feedback in behavioral growth and skill acquisition.[78, 118] Without feedback, indicating what was correctly performed and what was less than adequate, practice would be rudderless. Imagine practicing a baseball swing without any coaching on modifying and perfecting technique—improvement would be difficult indeed! Feedback is what shapes and promotes growth. Without it, practice can be an exercise in repetition of mistakes, stagnation, and, often, extreme frustration.

In a sense, feedback should be given throughout the Teaching Interaction. Such feedback would focus on the student's cooperation, effort, calmness, participation, processing, persistence, patience, attention, and other "learning how to learn" targets. The feedback step of the TI session, however, follows the practice. In it, the teacher provides specific feedback on the student's performance, both positive and corrective. The key is specificity: Information on how the learner performed all (or as many as possible) of the components that were described and demonstrated should be provided. Positives should be sincere, accurate, and specific. Corrective feedback should be unambiguous, yet supportive and constructive. Presentation of feedback on "learning how to learn" targets can, of course, be included; indeed, it may be of particular importance if the student struggled with skill performance but still cooperated, participated, and tried.

Feedback

- Positive and corrective
- Specificity is key
- Skill performance and "learning how to learn" are targeted
- Cycle back to other TI components as indicated

Feedback may cycle back to the description/demonstration portion of the TI session as necessary. For example, corrective feedback can involve remodeling of specific skill components (e.g., "Your body seemed relaxed when you asked for help, but your face still seemed tense. Watch how it looks to have a relaxed body *and* face."). Opportunities for additional practice (with additional feedback) often follow. There may even be a cycling back to the rationale segment, with reasons given for the correct performance and for the inclusion of the particular element being retaught. This step would then be followed by additional modeling and practice as indicated.

Optional External Consequence

It is not uncommon for the feedback segment to be accompanied or followed by the giving of external reinforcement. Such reinforcement may take the form of tokens; direct reinforcement with items, activities, or opportunities; use of a contingency contract; or provision of other artificial motivators. It could involve reinforcement of social skill performance and/or appropriate "learning how to learn" behavior. On some occasions, discouraging or reductive consequences may be provided (e.g., response cost, withholding of positive outcomes), but they would almost always be applied based on the appearance of interfering or disruptive behavior and not as responses to difficulties in skill performance.

The giving of external consequences may serve important motivational functions. While praise and positive feedback may have some value for the student with ASD, they may not be sufficient to motivate participation, performance, and skill acquisition. Without sufficient motivation, learning and application of new skills may not occur. Conversely, without skill instruction, all of the motivation in the world is not likely to result in changed performance. Instruction and consequences are the two sides of the skill development coin. Using external, meaningful consequences will help ensure that the student is motivated.

Further, use of external contingencies at the end of a TI session may tie skill performance to the contingencies to be provided for using the targeted skill outside the teaching session. In a sense, the teacher indicates that this behavior will be reinforced not only in the simulation, but also—through the student's motivational arrangement (e.g., token economy)—when it appears throughout the learner's day.

External Consequence

- Ties into the student's motivational system
- Might involve either positive or corrective (for problem behavior) consequences
- Strengthens motivation
- Bridges to usage outside of teaching
- Enhances feedback
- Individually applied

Skilled use of external consequences can include providing "natural" outcomes. That is, the teacher can provide a reinforcer that represents what are likely, positive results of using a skill (e.g., for successfully performing good sportsmanship skills during a TI, the student is reinforced with an opportunity to play again—an example of a natural outcome of good sportsmanship). Not only does this reinforcement strategy readily lead to fading of artificial consequences, but it also offers a way for the student to experience the rationale in action.

Finally, external, differential reinforcement most definitely serves as feedback, underscoring and adding power and specificity to the verbal feedback provided by the teacher.

Given their many benefits, external consequences may be a customary part of Teaching Interactions for students. The application of this component, like all good ABA, depends on appropriateness, need, and flexible decision making on the part of the teacher.

A Few Other Points and Considerations

This section offers several additional recommendations and considerations related to Teaching Interactions that will help with the effective application of this teaching methodology.

Keep in Mind the Length of the TI Session

There is no rule regarding how long a TI session should be. Factors that may influence the length of a session include schedule limitations of the teaching setting, momentum showed by the learner, fatigue, and the amount that the student has learned. The most effective course of action in some instances is to end a session when a skill element or component has been mastered (ending on a positive note). If the session is not going as planned (e.g., the skill was not broken down sufficiently to promote learner success), then it may make sense to end the session, revise the teaching plan, and return to the skill at a later point. It certainly does not make sense to extend a session by repeatedly having a student role-play a skill when little or no progress is occurring or until all the life has gone out of the session.

Keep Prompts to a Minimum

As opposed to Discrete Trial Teaching,[65] Teaching Interactions involve limited use of prompts. If a student is having difficulty with an element of a skill, other techniques and strategies are more likely to be used than prompts. The other approaches may be more natural, produce more independence, and be more dignifying. They include strategies and techniques such as breaking the skill down further, shaping (i.e., differential reinforcement of successive approximations to the target behavior),[118] and backward or forward chaining (i.e., progressively connecting the elements of a task or skill together).[118]

Tailor the Language

For those children who have enough language to learn using a Teaching Interaction, but whose comprehension (receptive language) may still be limited, it is important for the teacher to tailor downward the amount of language provided within the TI session. Also, if a child has sufficient but limited expressive language, then the communication that is expected from the student during the TI should be adjusted downward as well. In addition, the language used for the rationale and for the description of the skill should be tailored to the child's age level and the peer culture surrounding the child.

Make It Fun

As with any teaching, it is important that, as much as is fitting and possible, learning is made enjoyable and fun. Suggestions for how teachers can accomplish this include building rapport, being positive and enthusiastic, using humor, being creative, and making both role-plays and demonstrations fresh and enjoyable.

Make It Natural and Individualized

Throughout the Teaching Interaction, it is important that the teacher make the teaching as natural as possible. For example, the teacher should use natural language, provide everyday examples of the behavior, and make the demonstration and role-plays as real as possible. Related to this point is the importance of gearing the session (including the teaching style used) to the specific student involved in the TI. As is true for all good teaching methodologies, one style of delivery does not fit all.

Develop Your Own Voice

Teaching Interactions work best when they have a natural feel and reflect genuine interaction. When the teacher incorporates his or her own style into the session the TI works best. When this occurs, rapport development is a usual side benefit as well.

Consider Both Formal and Informal TIs

The TI can certainly be done in a structured manner. In many cases, it will start with a clear statement—something like "Let's do a TI." While it is recommended that TI sessions include all the necessary steps, sometimes teaching may look more like a discussion (or "buddy chat") than a formal TI session. This kind of interaction may occur in less formal, nonschool settings or with older students. Such "buddy chats" can barely seem like a TI to the naked eye and seem to have a very natural flow. In fact, such "discussions," upon closer examination, still include the critical steps of the TI procedure, but are embedded in a typical-looking and -feeling conversation. During such informal TIs, the teacher would not announce that a session is being initiated, nor would the steps be noted. Instead rationales, descriptions, and demonstrations and even practice would occur in a more naturally flowing discussion format.

Example:

TEACHER: Hey, Al.

STUDENT: Hello, Ms. Norton.

TEACHER: How have things been?

STUDENT: Not so bad. Reached fifth level on *Starfox*. Would spend more time on it but too much homework.

TEACHER: How is your homework going?

STUDENT: Okay, but am bummed about my math work. It is very, very hard.

TEACHER: Math is very hard. You know, I am a little bummed, too. I tried to get help **[Label]** from my supervisor, but I messed up and now don't know what to do **[Rationale]**. That ever happen to you?

STUDENT: I suppose.

TEACHER: When I try to get help from someone I always mess it up—it comes out like this **[Demonstration of wrong way]**. I don't know what I am doing wrong.

STUDENT: You're yelling!

TEACHER: Really? How would you do it? **[beginning Practice]** The informal TI would proceed from there.

Decisions to conduct a more informal TI session or a more formal, structured one are based on a variety of factors, including the skill being taught, issues that might increase the participation of the learner, the timing of the session, and the relationship between the teacher and learner.

Think About the Timing of the TI Session

It may make sense for some TIs to be conducted at the time that a need is shown (e.g., right after a problematic social situation occurred). The benefit of such an approach is that the rationale for the instruction is fresh and potent. However, on many occasions, the student may still be experiencing the after-effects of the problem situations right after its occurrence, and may not be fully available for teaching or may be highly sensitive to the issues involved. In such cases, delaying the TI to a time of greater availability and distance from the incident is highly advisable.

Move on with Mastery

As with all systematic instruction, TI work gradually moves forward by expanding skills, adding challenge and complexity, and promoting independent usage in natural circumstances. However, as in all good teaching, it is important to not to move ahead before the student has achieved mastery at the present level of instruction.

Bridge the Session

It is a good practice to end a TI session with a statement that bridges the instruction to future effort or performance. This certainly sets up the possibility of generalization (discussed later in the chapter) and indicates to the student that the TI is not about just one simple step or performance during a role-play. Statements such as "Let's try this some more another time," "We will add some more parts the next time we practice," or "I think you are ready to try this [for example] during recess" help the student understand that the work is to extend beyond the TI session.

Discrimination Training

Discrimination training has long been used as an instructional method for social skills.[111] It can be used, as a larger part of the Teaching Interaction methodology, before, during, and/or after a TI session as described previously. It may be used to help the student tell the difference between appropriate/correct (sometimes referred to as "cool") and inappropriate/incorrect ("not cool") versions or parts (e.g., body posture, voice intonation, facial expression) of a skill. During such training, the teacher provides examples of the forms of the behavior (e.g., in vivo, pictorially, through video modeling), and the student learns to correctly identify the category of the response (e.g., cool or not cool, polite or impolite, bored or interested). A Discrete Trial Teaching[65] format (individual or group), including prompting and prompt fading, works especially well for such training.

Discrimination Training

- Before, during, and after TI sessions
- DTT methodology
- Elements of skills
- Whole skills
- Reading of social cues
- "Living rationales"

Discrimination training can also be used to help the student better identify the social cues of others (see the discussion of social awareness in Chapter 8). Further, discrimination training can be used to bolster the rationale step of the Teaching Interaction. Using examples, the student can be shown how positive outcomes result from the use of new skills. This can be contrasted with examples of inappropriate behaviors resulting in clearly undesirable outcomes. Such "living rationales" can clarify abstract rationale concepts.

Generalization Training

None of the social skills instruction work has true value if it does not result in consistent, independent usage by the student in everyday, real-life situations. When skills are taught in a structured, artificial setting but never taken any further than that, the critical purpose of teaching social skills has been lost. Generalization training is the method by which skills are transferred from role-play to natural circumstances. In ASD (and really in any good teaching), such transfer will rarely occur without systematic generalization efforts.[116] If one thinks about it, role-plays are conducted so that instruction can occur far removed from the challenges, complexities, and interferences of naturally occurring situations. Such removal, however, grossly reduces the likelihood of transfer. The goal is to gradually, over time, blur the distinction between the artificial role-play situation and the natural use of the skill. This means gradually making the role-plays increasingly more realistic as well as gradually moving the teaching into naturally occurring contexts and situations. It also means systematically planning the transfer of artificial, external reinforcement to natural reinforcement (what had been discussed as rationales).

As part of the overall Teaching Interaction methodology, generalization training includes gradually transfer of the skill to natural situations along a number of dimensions. Several typical domains of transfer are described here:

1. **People.** At first, the Teaching Interaction sessions usually involve participants who increase the likelihood of successful practice and acquisition of skills. If appropriate, over time individuals are included who represent more challenging and/or typical persons. For example, if

a student is having a hard time handling the inappropriate behavior of a peer, the TI sessions may begin with an adult, then switch to a peer who is a friend of the student, then include an acquaintance, and eventually include the provocative individual. As another example, if a male student is learning to initiate conversation with a member of the opposite sex (to whom he is attracted), practice may begin with a male friend, then switch to a female one, and eventually take place with the particular and special girl.

2. **Place.** It may be that the skill being taught needs to occur in specific (and perhaps challenging) locales and situations (e.g., during recess). In such a case, work moves from comfortable locations and situations to more natural ones.

3. **Time.** Particular times of the week or day (or specific events) may be the most challenging for using the skill. Work gradually moves to those times.

4. **Provocativeness.** It is often the case that skills must be used under trying or demanding social circumstances. In this situation, work begins with minimal provocation and moves into real-life, authentic challenge. For example, if the goal is teaching a student how to respond to the teasing of others, then mild, innocuous statements would initially be used and gradually and progressively instruction would involve comments and actions that hit vulnerable and sensitive spots.

5. **Predictability.** Life comes at you unexpectedly. One of the biggest obstacles to independent usage of learned skills relates to predictability. Role-plays are not only make-believe, but also, by their very nature, create preparedness. Gradually, the opportunity for the use of the skill needs to be presented unexpectedly. This can be done, for example, through initial priming (pre-situation reminders) and the fading of such priming by presenting the situation longer and longer periods of time after the reminder (and the eventual fading of all reminders).

6. **General Authenticity.** For all the other aspects and characteristics of role-plays—that is, the things that make them make-believe—effort should be directed at making the sessions and skill opportunities more realistic, naturalistic, and authentic.

7. **Reinforcement.** External reinforcement is often employed during the Teaching Interaction sessions. These contingencies highlight to the student the appropriate behavior to be utilized, reinforce correct performance, and increase motivation to participate in the teaching session. However, generalization to a natural environment, which is free from artificial, external reinforcement, needs to eventually occur. For this transfer to happen, a systematic fading of the external reinforcement is necessary. Setting up situations to increase the probability of the occurrence of natural support and reinforcement, especially as work is gradually faded to everyday situations, can be helpful.

The idea in generalization training is to gradually move the skill performance into skill usage in naturally occurring situations. Given that many of the previously discussed dimensions may be involved, this means moving between domains carefully and gradually. If the skill involved teaching someone how to drive a manual transmission, to be successful we might begin in an empty, flat, supermarket parking lot. Even with some success there, we would not, however, immediately move to a busy expressway. Instead, we might gradually move to a flat street with no other cars around, then to a busier yet flat street, and then perhaps to a street with some incline—but when we did so, we would initially practice on a street with no traffic on it. Eventually we might move to a street that had inclines and traffic, but we might also practice using more than one car (with a different feel to the clutch and transmission) but return to a less traveled street when we first did so. We might even have different numbers of passengers (including none) in the car as well as a range of different road conditions, as we gradually and progressively moved our way up to the ultimate goal of independent and competent operation of a car with a manual transmission (and expressway driving).

This is the same approach we would use in generalization training involving Teaching Interactions targeting social skills. We may work within a specific domain, gradually progressing through its continuum. Because more than one dimension may be involved, we might also work between domains, sometimes dropping down a few levels in one domain as we introduce another. The ultimate goal is not only to develop authentic skills, but also to promote independent and successful usage in real-life social situations. This is the core objective of the various and powerful elements of the Teaching Interaction approach.

3
Social Skills Groups

Mitchell Taubman and Ron Leaf

What Is Typical?

We have had the opportunity to visit many social skills groups over the years, including classroom-based programs, lunch groups, and therapy groups at clinics. Typically, when we observe social skills groups, this is what we see:

- Opening routines in which participants discuss topics like their day or upcoming weekend plans.
- Social "lessons" (e.g., what it takes to be a good friend, how to ask someone to play) covered by the whole group. These might involve lectures by the facilitator and discussions.
- Social Stories based on the assumption that a child with autism spectrum disorder (ASD) can learn complex social skills through simply listening to or reading a story.
- A social exercise that might include worksheets or role-play.
- A social activity that might involve a table-top game or outside play.

The individual who runs the group (perhaps a teacher, aide, or specialist) oversees the group and often has a central role in keeping things on track as well as providing correct information, answers, and guidance in the activities. The groups may meet on schedules ranging from daily to once a week. They are most often made up of young people who are considered "higher functioning" but are still quite variable in their social skills and abilities.

Let's take a minute and examine this arrangement. Suppose that this was not a social skills group but rather a math club—that is, a group designed to provide tutoring work in mathematics. Would activities that are the same for everyone be of individual benefit to students with a wide variety of math challenges? Would general, preplanned (often canned) lesson plans address students' individual math needs? Would simply doing math exercises make a difference, or would an individualized, structured approach to building math skills be necessary? Would reading a story about someone who is good at math improve the participants' own math skills? Would repeated reminders, prompts, assistance, guidance, and facilitation related to those math activities and lessons make the students independently good at math? Would a strong dependency on the club facilitator somehow make them more independent? And would you really expect that math abilities that are worked on only at club meetings would somehow transfer to the classroom and usage in everyday life?

To truly be effective, such a math club would need to make sure that individual needs are identified and individual skills are taught. Further, transfer of independent skills out of the club and into the classroom and the real world would be a must. Why, then, would we expect anything else for clubs that address needs in the social area?

The Realities of Social Skill Instruction for Individuals with Autism

Children with ASD do not readily pick up social skills merely through exposure to others with those competencies.[66] It is also the case that ongoing guidance, facilitation, and assistance (prompts or help that is never faded) do not produce independent social growth. Our experience[91] has been that this holds true for all individuals with ASD. What children need is careful and systematic instruction to build social behavior, whether simple or complex. Further, and perhaps most critical, growth in the social area cannot be expected to broadly and generally occur when work happens only once or twice a week (or even once or twice a day!) in isolated groups.

Requirements for social skills occur throughout a child's day; likewise, training should occur throughout the day. Further, transfer to everyday situations and life cannot and will not occur when social skills training takes place only in groups, clubs, or similar arrangements. Specific and systematic training is necessary to transfer skill development from clubs and other unique arrangements into "battlefield" conditions.

Necessary Ingredients for Social Skills Groups

Let's take a brief look at the essential elements of social skills training groups. This overview will be followed by a more in-depth discussion of their workings.

- Individualized assessment of needs (and of progress)
- Individualized instructional content (and programmatic methods as appropriate)
- Trained staff who provide true and systematic programming and instruction
- Programming and instruction designed to produce authentic, independent competencies
- Focus on active and experiential learning
- A configuration that diminishes the centrality of the group's teacher/facilitator
- Development and implementation of plans that spread and promote the work throughout the child's day and facilitate transfer of learned skills to everyday social life

Individualized Assessment of Needs and Progress

Each child with ASD is unique; each has his or her own set of strengths and weaknesses. This is especially true in the social area. To work in an individualized manner on social competencies, one must have a sense of where the student is at. That point seems so obvious that it's hard to imagine it has to be written. Yet, such an assessment occurs all too rarely, on even an informal basis, in most social groups.

This book's chapters on assessment and curriculum development (Chapters 6 and 7) can help here. Ours is not an argument for extensive, formal assessment or data collection. Rather, there is a need to obtain a sense of how children are functioning across a variety of relevant areas (see Chapter 8 on the social skills taxonomy) as they enter the group and as they progress while participating.

Individualized Instructional Methods and Content

While some content (e.g., social skill themes) and methods (e.g., group-wide token economies) may be common to all members of the group, individualization of programming is critical. Each child with ASD has unique social skills deficits and, therefore, requires individualized systematic instruction for acquisition of the necessary skills. This is no different than any other area of deficit. Without careful, progressive, and individualized programming, students will not be successful. Likewise, a uniquely tailored treatment program may be necessary for individual children. Some require Discrete Trial Teaching[65] for instruction in social skills, whereas others may respond well to Teaching Interactions (see Chapter 2). Some children may be learning complex skills in highly structured arrangements, whereas others focus on applying learned skills in the natural environment. Some may need complex motivation systems for learning and using new skills, whereas others are internally motivated. Individualization is essential.

Trained Staff

You might already be getting the idea that this can be pretty elaborate stuff—and you would be right. Social skills are complicated matters, and they are not usually just "absorbed" by children with ASD. Quality social groups require work and sophistication.[49] Staff ability is critical to such endeavors. Running a social group that will produce genuine, meaningful improvements in social skills involves more than simply providing appealing social activities and herding students through them. The individuals who run a social group will need to be trained to competency in providing complex and systematic programming and in achieving this objective with several children simultaneously. Board Certified Behavior Analyst (BCBA) accreditation is usually neither necessary nor sufficient to meet these goals.

Authenticity and Independence

As noted previously, coordinating a group of children with social skills needs can be daunting. It might be easy and tempting to take shortcuts. Assisting, facilitating, and guiding (i.e., prompting that is never faded) the children through performance of activities will help the group move along smoothly and get the children to perform social behaviors in the moment. Teaching scripts and rote social responses to the group's children may ease the burden. Reading a social story that does not incorporate practice and feedback (which would actually be a Teaching Interaction) may occupy the children with social matters during the group. Unfortunately, none of this results in the learning of genuine, independent social skills. If that is the true objective of a social group (and we really can't imagine what the objective would be otherwise), then such strategies should be used sparingly.

Sometimes, for example, it is necessary to take practical measures (have some guided activities) to facilitate the establishment of a group. Effort should be taken to reduce such tactics over time, however, and to ensure that real skills instruction is occurring. In ASD, there is no substitute for systematic programming, including actual teaching, whether occurring in one-on-one instruction or a social group. Moreover, independent, fluid, authentic skills are not acquired through shortcuts.

Active and Experiential Learning

We don't know about you, but we did not learn how to drive a car with a manual transmission by reading a driving story, or by sitting at a desk and plowing through worksheets—or by taking part in discussions, for that matter. Watching golf videos, reading a golf manual, or just playing with a professional would not likely result in one becoming a scratch golfer, either. Why would we expect matters to be any different for social skills?

Graduated instruction, under increasingly realistic and complex situations, is key to genuine learning of social skills for the ASD population. Social groups should be filled with fun social activities and experiences—some made-up and some real. Typically developing children should be involved when appropriate and to the extent possible. Coordinated and related effort outside of the group, in the child's real world, should be included as well. Again, the group should not just focus on engaging social activities; rather, it should incorporate fun with a purpose and a program. Concentrated effort or even one-on-one instruction may be included in the teaching plan. Nevertheless, the teaching of social skills during fun and compelling social activities (embedded programming) accounts for the lion's share of successful social groups for children with ASD.

Centrality of the Staff

Staff roles in social skills groups can be a little confusing. In classes, we often work hard to have a student with ASD rely on the aide less and less and the teacher more and more. In social groups, whether run by teachers, aides, therapists, or other staff, the idea is for the children to look to those individuals decreasingly over time. Yes, the children will need instruction from the adult. Yes, the staff will need to maintain order and reduce chaos. However, staff members must work hard at not being too necessary; they should be careful to ensure that the children don't learn to depend on, interact with, and refer to the adults too much.

Children with ASD need to learn to independently interact with one another, not just with an adult when peers are around. They need to learn to independently apply skills in social situations, not depend on the support and guidance of adults. Staff must increasingly direct effort at fading their presence and having the children utilize, as well as interact with, one another. Staff also need to work hard at fading prompts, artificiality, and structure and moving skills into natural situations—over time, making themselves increasingly irrelevant.

Transfer of Skills Beyond the Group

Social skills cannot be learned at a desk, and application of social skills cannot be learned by a child with ASD merely taking part in a group meeting for two hours twice a week. Social skills programming must occur, in concentrated and embedded fashion, throughout the child's day—at home and in school, in karate class and at picnics, in the park and at grandma's and grandpa's house. Further, generalization training must occur so that social skills learned in social groups will be used in natural, everyday social situations. Transfer cannot be expected to happen magically, nor can transfer efforts occur in a willy-nilly fashion. Instead, generalization programming needs to be planned and systematic. This does not mean just helping students use skills in other rooms and with other kids; rather, it means programming training so that skills can gradually be used in increasingly authentic and challenging situations (see Chapter 2 on Teaching Interactions).

For any of this to occur, efforts need to be broad and coordinated. Staff working with social skills groups must communicate and coordinate in open and ongoing ways with other staff, school personnel, and family members. Regular, periodic team meetings are critical for input and output, program development, review of efforts, adjustments, and general interventional dissemination and oversight. And, of course, collaboration is essential.

An Example

Let's see how some of this coordinated activity might look. Suppose Debbie is an elementary special education teacher who runs a social skills group every afternoon, attended by five of her students with ASD and two reverse-mainstreamed typically developing students. What follows is a list of the five students, and a few of their social needs. Each need is coded with a letter. Following that is a description of the social skills group's programming, with the code letters included. In this way, the approach used to address each of the students' needs (through whole-group, individual, concentrated, or embedded teaching) is highlighted. First the list of the students:

- Ben: [A]Reading the nonverbal social communication of others; [B]being assertive.
- Rob: [C]When he is talking to others, knowing how they are reacting, including if they are interested or bored in what he has to say; [D]initiating social interactions.
- Mary: Reading the nonverbal cues of others; [F]interrupting.
- Ken: [G]Being aware of who is in the immediate social environment; [H]responding to the initiations of others.

Because all of her students have difficulties in social awareness (see the discussion in Chapter 8), Debbie decides to do a whole set of group lessons on reading social cues. The activities will essentially comprise social cue discrimination tasks (see Chapter 2). The general education students and occasionally one of her students (especially Rob) act out prewritten scenarios. and the remaining students identify the social cues the participants are displaying (e.g., whether they are bored or interested, being rigid or flexible, excited or calm)[A, C, E]. Debbie will use a token economy she has established for all the students to reward correct answers as well as the quality of their responses (e.g., for good attention, engaged, enthusiastic participation, problem solving).

During this task, Ken will not be expected to identify the social cues. He will be asked to vocally and nonvocally identify who is participating at the front of the room[G]. At times, he will be reinforced by a typical peer (and be given further reinforcement for actively accepting such reward)[H]. In time, Ken will also be asked questions by one of the typical peers[H Generalization].

Ben and Mary will not only be required to identify the social cues, but also asked to describe which verbal and nonverbal cues helped them come up with the right answer[A, E].

On occasion, the teacher will insist that Ben is wrong, even when he is right[B]. She will use the opportunity to teach him the steps of being assertive[B] using a Teaching Interaction approach (see Chapter 2). Debbie will make her initial assertions exaggerated and obvious, but gradually make them less so over time[B Generalization]. Eventually, a peer will disagree as well[B Generalization].

In time, role-plays will involve subjects that include themes of great interest to Mary. She will be reinforced from refraining from blurting or jumping into these discussions as, over time, material is included that is more and more compelling to her[F and Generalization].

As noted previously, Rob will get a chance to role-play the scenarios at the front of the room, with these opportunities coming more often over time so that he can also practice initiation with peers[D]. Gradually, less information guiding his part will be provided to him, and his initiation of the role-play will depend on the actions or activity of the other role-player[D Generalization].

With practice and success, Debbie will begin to set up opportunities for each of the students to use their emerging skills outside of the social cues lesson and eventually outside of the social skills group[Further Generalization].

As can easily be seen, there is much going on in this activity: layering of both group and individualized programming as well as a lot of teaching on a lot of targets occurring throughout. All of this learning occurs systematically, so that skills are progressively broadened and moved to independent and natural usage. In essence, there is a bit of planning and a lot of choreography. The result, however, is a social skills group that produces real learning and independent social skills use.

It Takes Time

Just like Rome, quality social skills groups are not built in a day. They, like most other programmatic efforts with children with ASD, are a process. Developed and nurtured with care, such groups not only become entities of quality service, but also evolve into groupings with their own style, culture, and personality. They become groups that not only promote substantial social growth, but also reflect the growing social abilities and relationships of their participants—and that is a nice thing indeed.

4

Socialization and Adolescence

Tracee Parker

Typical Social Development

Adolescence is a tremulous developmental period for most teens, serving as the gateway between childhood and adulthood. This passage is certainly not "toll free"; rather, it is laden with intense physical, emotional, physiological, attitudinal, and behavioral changes. Although this period is often stressful, confusing, and frustrating, typical adolescents commonly find solace in knowing that they aren't alone (i.e., peers and friends struggle in facing the same challenges). Through this shared experience, they may seek out and "compare notes" with more knowledgeable and mature peers. They also access media and may utilize problem-solving skills to achieve intrapersonal growth, autonomy, and social competence.

Social relationships across the board (with family, friends and romantic interests) are in a perpetual state of motion. During adolescence, adults become less important, while peers gain paramount social significance. Emotional separation from adults and alignment with peers is a hallmark of this period. As a result, adolescents begin forming their own perspectives, values, morals, and opinions, independent and often distinct from their parents. In fact, many are quite outspoken in expressing divergent opinions on issues that are important to them.

The developmental "job" of an adolescent is striving to achieve autonomy, independence, and a sense of the youth's own individual identity. In this process, adolescents often bump up against adult-imposed limits and rules. It is more the norm, than not, for them to reject restrictions (often quite strongly) that they feel they have outgrown or that challenge their autonomy. Displays of disrespect for authority, disregard of rules, extreme (seemingly irrational) emotional reactions, and rejection of adult control are commonplace during adolescence. Suddenly, all the guidelines that once shaped expectations for how typical children should behave fly out the window.

Most typical adolescents have already acquired social reciprocity, compassion, and perspective taking. However, they may consciously choose to disregard such qualities, due to a sometimes intense focus on themselves: "It's all about ME!!"

Adolescence is also characterized by feelings of invulnerability, struggles with impulse control, and challenges related to delay of gratification. Until late adolescence, their vision tends to be idealized, while their immediate actions are not specifically goal directed. In turn, adolescents are often conflicted owing to their desire for freedom, but a general lack of readiness to embrace the responsibility that goes with it. Resolving this struggle is another essential developmental milestone of adolescence.

Ultimately, most adolescents start thinking about the long term—that is, their future, goals, and society around them. They gradually accept more personal responsibility for orchestrating many aspects of daily life. For example, they may take charge of their own scheduling and transportation (i.e., planning for social functions, assignments and school work) and even seek part-time jobs that enable them to gain some degree of financial independence. Further, motivated by their desire to form and maintain relationships, they eventually come to realize and experience the necessity of consideration and concern for others.

Social Development and Autism Spectrum Disorder

Sociocultural Considerations

Behaviorally speaking, our social development, knowledge, attitudes, emotional reactions, and behaviors are shaped by our environment, through the process of learning[79,118]. Simplistically, what we know and how we view, feel about, and interact with the world and people in it result from our collective life experiences, beginning from the time we are born. Those experiences are influenced by who we spend our time with, how we are perceived and treated, opportunities we are given (or not), and the results of actions we take.

Research demonstrates that environment affects all or most areas of functioning, including social development. Comparatively, a more typical (versus atypical) environment shapes social behavior, knowledge, and perspectives that are more similar to mainstream society.

Although physical locale influences this process, for the most part it is *not* primarily about environmental setting per se. For example, in regular education classes, children with disabilities are often perceived and treated in a manner that is divergent from their peers. In contrast, special needs children in segregated settings may be regarded and taught to behave in such a way that approximates their typical peers.

In this context, "sociocultural considerations" refers to the fact that merely having a disability affects how others view and treat a person. This "culture" exists and develops as a result of others' perspectives, expectations, and beliefs about autism spectrum disorder (ASD) and other developmental disabilities. Sadly, many of these perceptions are erroneous. Indeed, there is a tendency even among parents and professionals to hold lower social expectations for children with ASD as compared to their typical peers.

Adults commonly regard and treat children with ASD as younger, and less socially capable, than they are. This perspective often leads to problematic outcomes:

- Restricting opportunities for independence and decision making
- Excusing unacceptable behavior because "the child has social deficits due to the disability, so what can you expect?"
- Placing a lower priority on socialization (needs, interests, and desires), over more task-oriented or academic pursuits

Disavowing the importance of social development may alleviate pressure to address social skills, which are more challenging to teach. To be sure, the content of basic, concrete social skills—especially those required in a classroom—is commonly taught. For example, children with ASD routinely learn to respond to greetings, orient themselves to others, share items, and wait their turn. In contrast, the far more critical and complex socialization (process) skills are frequently neglected.

What do we mean by "more critical" and "socialization process" skills? These are not a simple, concrete series of steps performed in predictable and easily identified contexts. Rather, they are pivotal social processes applied across a variety of diverse and ever-changing situations. They cannot be taught as rote lessons, but instead require the individual to acquire and apply authentic understanding of social dynamics. Examples would include problem solving, assertion, understanding social alliances, relationship reciprocity, and empathy (see Chapter 8 and the Curriculum section in this book). Aside from the challenges presented by these skills' inherent complexity, opportunities for children with ASD to apply and practice these skills with peers become increasingly difficult to arrange as children mature.

The cumulative outcome of these sociocultural influences is that the children tend to fall progressively further behind norms of typical social development and behavior. As "children" with ASD approach adolescence, they are already "walking in" (usually middle school) at a grave disadvantage.

ASD and Adolescence: A Secondary Disorder

Upon reaching their teenage years, children with ASD acquire a secondary disorder—namely, "adolescence." As noted previously, these youths experience emotional, physiological, and behavioral turmoil commensurate with their peers. However, adolescents with ASD commonly lack the awareness and knowledge to understand the underlying sources and meaning of these changes. The "toll" of this gateway on children with ASD can be far greater than for their typical peers, in part because they are missing essential concepts, experiences, skill requisites, and fluency. Additionally, they don't have access to the same resources, peer support, or relationships as are available to typical children.

If the adolescent with ASD has received treatment services during childhood, his or her therapists likely will have spent years teaching cooperative and socially acceptable behavior (e.g., "cool/not cool"). But now, "cool" may mean "not cool" (i.e., antagonistic attitudes or indifferent behavior that teachers previously discouraged). "Acting out," to some degree, is the norm for adolescents. Being passive and highly compliant may *not* be typical at this stage of development, while testing and pushing the limits often is! The whole template of what we attempted to teach as "typical and appropriate" in many cases has now been flipped upside down.

To illustrate:

Question: How can you pick out the student with ASD in a high school class?
Answer: He's the one with his nose buried in a book doing exactly what he's supposed to.

A perpetually vicious cycle prevails: The ever-widening gap in assertiveness, social judgment, and functional independence leads adults to further reduce expectations and responsibilities of adolescents with ASD and solidify their view of these youths as eternally "young children." In turn, overprotection, excessive restrictions of freedom, and dependency on adults become the norm. This dynamic, coupled with their significant social skills deficiencies, renders these children unprepared for adult life and causes them to miss out on essential life experiences for learning personal responsibility, autonomy, and social independence.

Adolescent life exists within a hostile and daunting social world. Just coping and surviving taxes all emotional reserves. As difficult as their peers' "socialization dance" was to follow during childhood, it is now 100 times more complex, obtuse, and periodically "anti-rule" governed.

Understanding the social relationships, networks, mechanisms, and dynamics as well as the subtle nuances of "adolescent culture," which are essential for successful peer socialization, can be beyond the grasp or abilities of many adolescents with ASD. As a result, many fail to form social bonds, leaving them out of the "teen milieu" and at a severe disadvantage without the emotional support afforded by their peers.

Lacking access to peer influences, these children don't develop their own independent opinions, values, morals, confidence, initiative, or sense of autonomous identity. The lost opportunities to navigate these critical adolescence milestones equates to "failure in accomplishing their developmental job" (objectives). As their peers achieve ever-increasing autonomy and competence, the social backslide for children with ASD can accelerate.

Although lacking insight (as to the cause), many higher-functioning children *are* aware of this widening gap, which in turn contributes to their sense of social failure, helplessness, confusion, frustration, and promotion of social isolation. Not surprisingly, adolescents with ASD tend to shy even further away from socializing with peers, creating perpetual reliance on adults (e.g., family members, aides, caregivers, service providers) to fill this social void. Most unfortunately, such relationships with adults are utterly inadequate substitutes for peer relationships.

Critical differences exist in the nature and dynamics of relationships with adults versus with peers. With few exceptions, there is a distinct imbalance of power and influence, most of which is held by adults (authority figures) over children and adolescents. Aside from the advantages deriving from their physical size, adults control access to basic needs, resources, privileges, finances, and other aspects of life relative to children. Moreover, as children, we come to rely on adults to validate, support, and care for us emotionally. Fear of losing these "commodities" enables adults to exert a certain degree of control over children's lives, decisions, and behavior.

By their very nature, "adult–child" social relationships are unidirectional ("one-way streets"). Parents, teachers, and professionals are expected to "be there," regardless of how "the child" behaves, acts toward them, or treats them. Such a dynamic limits the incentive to acquire and apply social reciprocity, perspective taking, sensitivity, and other relationship-critical skills. Without peer relationships, adolescents with ASD do not experience an intrinsic drive to develop reciprocation of social support and other higher-order (compassion, consideration, altruism) skills and characteristics. Similarly, their motivation to care about what and how others think, feel, or perceive them is severely limited. They come to believe they will be accepted almost unconditionally, confirming their egocentric and highly stilted view.

Sometimes, once persons with ASD pass through their adolescence, they have missed too many years of critical socialization lessons to catch up. When this happens, their chance for a satisfying and fulfilling adult social life is significantly reduced and their potential to develop future, meaningful adult relationships may be highly impacted.

Social/Sexual Development Overview

Social/sexual development is a significant, complex arena, and one that goes well beyond the scope of this chapter. However, it is impossible to adequately address the "true" nature of adolescent intrapersonal and interpersonal life without at least some discussion of the social/sexual component. Layering in sexual development on top of the myriad of adolescence challenges merely opens the door to more serious interpersonal, social, and even legal ramifications.

Talking to one's child about sexuality is uncomfortable for many parents, as well as for children. Few parents look forward to "opening the door" on discussing "sex" with their children. Some parents avoid this topic altogether and even deny seeing their children as "sexual." In schools, broaching the subject of sexuality is generally restricted to a formal sex education class. The traditional curriculum commonly contains anatomical and physiological facts and topics such as pubertal development, menstruation, reproduction, sexually transmitted diseases, and contraception.

With onset of puberty, all children experience significant internal and external biological changes. This physical maturation is associated with physiological processes, including an increase in sexual drive and sensations (e.g., arousal), which are manifested in young people's heightened sexual awareness, interest, exploration, and frustration. From a biological standpoint, children with ASD are no different from their cohorts. That is, the rate of their physical sexual development and the degree of their sexual drive are commensurate with those of their adolescent peers.

How any child responds, feels, and deals with this developmental transformation depends in part on how much the youth was prepared for it. Family, cultural, and religious values that have been imparted certainly play a role in perspective and emotional reactions to one's emerging sexuality. At least initially, sexual discovery commonly takes the form of solitary activities. However, interest and desire in pursuing this exploration with a partner are rarely far behind.

"Typical" Social/Sexual Development

It is probably safe to say few, if any, children are totally equipped to deal with their impending sexual development. To a great extent, preparedness is individually determined and dependent on a variety of factors. Typical children learn a great deal about standards of social/sexual behavior informally. No one sits them down or offers a class on rules of dating, consent, or flirtation. Rather, cultural norms and expectations of social/sexual practices, as well as subtle interpersonal rules, are acquired incidentally and through observation of those they identify with and look up to. As their adult counterparts once did in their own youth, typically developing children also research and access mainstream resources and media to broaden their understanding. In fact, this is probably an even more extensive practice for children today.

Most of today's adults did not rely on parents, teachers, or even formal sex education classes to gain the majority of their sexual knowledge and information. In fact, typically developing children commonly reject adult viewpoints as they struggle to form their own autonomous values, beliefs, and mores about sexual relationships and conduct. A preponderance of their foundational knowledge as well as depth of understanding comes from peers and their own personal, life experiences. If (or rather when) confused or frustrated, typical children seek out the "experts" for reassurance. They look to friends and more knowledgeable peers for guidance in handling and coping with these physical and emotional experiences. Similarly, as they initiate "the dating game," they rely on friends for support and advice in navigating the trials and tribulations of "boyfriend/girlfriend" relationships.

As they emerge from adolescence, typically developing individuals often enter young adulthood having had years of social/sexual learning "opportunities." That is, they will have benefited from a varied range and breadth of social/sexual experiences and relationships. They possess a foundation of essential skills and knowledge, forming the basis of their future intimate adult relationships.

Social/Sexual Development of Adolescents with ASD

Navigating the social waters of middle and high school is a daunting prospect for any student, and one that is fraught with numerous pitfalls. Their many socialization (process) deficits and "missed lessons" can present unique obstacles to adolescents with ASD in this regard, as they may lack the social skills that are foundational to achieving social/sexual maturation and facing these challenges. It comes as no surprise, then, that this cornerstone of emerging sexuality makes adolescence downright treacherous for students with ASD.

To an even greater extent than with typical adolescents, adults (e.g., parents and teachers) avoid discussing sexuality with children with ASD. Common "reasons" (in reality, largely rationalizations) for this omission include the following:

- "Children with ASD aren't aware of and have no interest in that."
- "They aren't developmentally ready or capable of handling it."
- "If we talk about it, they'll want to do it."
- "Informing children implies permission to engage in sexual behavior."
- "It's not a high priority, compared to academic pursuits."

Sound familiar?

The actual reasons underlying this avoidance tend to relate to the adult's own situation:

- Many adults feel far greater discomfort about the prospect of talking to children with ASD about sex than about tackling this topic with typically developing children.
- Many adults view children with ASD as "asexual" and deny that they are sexual beings.
- Many adults do not know how to approach, structure, or teach these complex concepts.
- Fear of controversy (owing to the nature of "sexuality and disabilities") discourages schools from offering functional social/sexual education.

Basically, adults tend to view the task of educating adolescents with ASD about human sexuality as challenging at best and very, very frightening.

Even with this avoidance, adults often express some common concerns about youths with ASD and sexuality:

- Fear of victimization
- Fear of pregnancy and disease
- Fear that adolescents might exhibit inappropriate sexual behavior

When adults do talk to adolescents with ASD about "sex," many provide false information, for the purpose of discouraging children's interest and exploration of their sexuality (e.g., "You can't kiss until you're 18 years of age"; "If you touch yourself, everyone will know"; "Your sheets are wet in the morning because you urinated").

Some children with ASD may be permitted to enroll in a mainstream sex education class. However, unlike their typical peers, many don't understand or grasp the information as presented. For those who do, anatomical and physiological facts are merely the tip of the iceberg and fail to address more essential understanding of social/sexual development and relationships.

If adolescents with ASD realize their knowledge is lacking or inaccurate, they generally cannot access resources and media to remedy this, unlike their typical peers. For those who can, the information may be too abstract or complex to comprehend or apply and in some cases even age or otherwise inappropriate (e.g., Internet pornography).

Additionally, children with ASD often do not absorb the lessons on social/sexual norms and practices. Such matters are nuanced, are subtle, and require complex skills (i.e., drawing inferences, social observation, incidental learning). Adding to these youths' challenges are their years of experience with others accommodating, excusing, and even contradicting critical societal norms (e.g. respecting privacy and personal space; disclosing personal information; regarding adult acquaintances as "friends"; allowing, or even encouraging, socializing with younger peers).

Once again, a crucial resource (peer relationships) useful for closing these gaps is often absent. Adults, being the primary social contacts for adolescents with ASD, offer little basis for navigating social/sexual peer relationships. Critical social/sexual skills are not learned, further compounding other deficits. Most unfortunately and resultantly, these children frequently miss out on common and core teenage experiences and opportunities.

Ultimately, this stunted development leaves children with ASD at *very* high risk for a variety of social/sexual problems, including exploitation by peers and sexual abuse at the hand of adults. Victimization by peers may take the form of being "set up" (i.e., to engage in unacceptable behavior) for amusement, teasing, and even being taken advantage of (sexually). It should not be surprising that the rate of sexual abuse (by adult perpetrators) is significantly higher for children with developmental disabilities.

Additionally, children with ASD are more likely to engage in or be accused of inappropriate sexual behavior, including violation of others' rights (e.g., touching, "stalking"), violation of social and school rules (e.g., exhibition of private behavior), and legal infractions. In some cases, the children are aware that their behavior is unacceptable, but lack the knowledge and skills to understand or fulfill normal needs in an acceptable manner. More often, they don't realize or comprehend the true nature or social impact of their actions. Related to this factor, it is commonplace for children with ASD to experience discrimination and violation of their personal rights, in varied forms. (There is an irony here: In part due to avoidance based on fear, adults' greatest worries sometimes come to fruition.)

Consultation Referral Examples

The following are examples of the content of routine referrals we have received for consultation services that illustrate typical responses to the social/sexual behavior of people with ASD.

REFERRAL 1: "Inappropriate Sexual Behavior"

FAMILY/SCHOOL: Reports special needs students are engaging in "inappropriate sexual behavior" with one another at school.

CONSULTANT: They're having sex at school?

FAMILY/SCHOOL: Of course not. They're "making out" and groping each other all over campus.

CONSULTANT: Really, in their classes?

FAMILY/SCHOOL: No, we'd never allow that. It's outside and between classes.

CONSULTANT: Okay, I understand. They're violating a school rule: No display of physical affection between students is permitted on campus, right?

FAMILY/SCHOOL: Uh, not exactly. There aren't really any "official" school rules.

CONSULTANT: Okay, it's actually a social rule. The other students know to refrain from this behavior.

FAMILY/SCHOOL: Well, er, uh, no. That's not quite true, either. I mean, come on, these [typical] children are high school students with raging hormones, but they're "discreet."

CONSULTANT: Okay, let me make sure I've got this straight. The "inappropriate sexual behavior" I was called to address is physical affection. The "identified" students are not breaking any "official" school rules or violating anyone's rights. With one subtle exception, their behavior is no different than the vast majority of children at this school. That exception is that the "target" students don't know to be "discreet." So the intervention plan is this: Teach them to read "unwritten fine print." Does that sum it up?

FAMILY/SCHOOL: Gee, yeah, I guess so.

REFERRAL 2: "Inappropriate Masturbation"

FAMILY/SCHOOL: Reports ASD student is "engaging in inappropriate, private behavior in class."

CONSULTANT: What is he doing?

FAMILY/SCHOOL: He gets an erection, and touches himself.

CONSULTANT: He's masturbating in class?

FAMILY/SCHOOL: No, we wouldn't let him do that. He gets aroused and then touches or pushes on it. Sometimes he stands up, where everyone can see. It's very uncomfortable, embarrassing.

CONSULTANT: I understand, he's trying to disturb the class or seek negative attention?

FAMILY/SCHOOL: Uh, not exactly. He gets agitated, and asks to use the bathroom excessively.

CONSULTANT: Okay, he's doing it to avoid the lesson, class work?

FAMILY/SCHOOL: Well, er, uh, that's not true, either. He's really into completing tasks.

CONSULTANT: I assume this doesn't happen with other (typical) students?

FAMILY/SCHOOL: I'm sure it does. But they "deal with it" so no one knows.

CONSULTANT: Okay, let me make sure I've got this straight. The "inappropriate masturbation" I was called to address is sexual arousal. The "identified" student is not seeking attention, trying to avoid work, or actually masturbating in class. He is experiencing sexual excitement (like his peers) but hasn't figured out the "tricks" for what to do about it. Does that sum it up?

FAMILY/SCHOOL: Gee, yeah, I guess so.

REFERRAL 3: "Inappropriate Touching"

FAMILY/SCHOOL: Reports student is "touching others inappropriately."

CONSULTANT: Do you mean grabbing people? Touching certain areas—genitals, breasts, and so on?

FAMILY/SCHOOL: Oh no, she hugs people whenever she greets them.

CONSULTANT: She does this with adults and peers?

FAMILY/SCHOOL: Well, it's been happening with adults for a while, but recently with peers.

CONSULTANT: Okay, so the adults discouraged this, but it escalated. That right?

FAMILY/SCHOOL: Uh, not exactly. She doesn't have friends. The staff didn't want her to feel rejected, so they let her hug them.

CONSULTANT: Okay, so adults allowed it but not the peers?

FAMILY/SCHOOL: Well, not really. She sees peers hug each other. They're nice children, and didn't want to be mean, so they allowed her to do it for a while.

CONSULTANT: Okay, but now they're telling her to "stop" and she is persisting?

FAMILY/SCHOOL: Well, er, uh, that's not true. They don't say anything because they don't want to hurt her feelings. They're obviously uncomfortable and told us [teachers] they want her to stop.

CONSULTANT: Okay, let me make sure I've got this straight. The "inappropriate touching" I was called to address is a social greeting "run amok." All parties—adults and peers—have encouraged (reinforced) hugging by allowing it. Now, they feel it's a problem, but gave no explicit "message" or feedback to her. And she missed their "obvious discomfort," which I assume means nonverbal cues. So intervention plan is this: teach her to read and interpret social cues. Does that sum it up?

FAMILY/SCHOOL: Gee, yeah, I guess so.

What's wrong with this picture?

All too frequently, adults and even peers "pathologize" typical adolescent behavior or social/sexual experience (e.g., arousal) where individuals with ASD are concerned. At the same time, problems are often shaped and reinforced when unacceptable behavior is permitted, ignored, encouraged, or excused due to "having a disability." When the behavior eventually becomes intolerable, these same adults (and peers) view the children with ASD as culpable, with the perceived solution being to "ameliorate the presumed problem behavior" (i.e., make it go away).

Such judgments are frequently biased and unjustified, and they fail to acknowledge both skill deficits and adults' and peers' role in perpetuating "problems." Regardless of the source, a student with ASD is certainly in need of proactive teaching ("lessons" we failed to provide). More importantly, the student is rarely the only—or even the primary—intervention target. Rather, the treatment plan warrants intervention on several fronts:

- Education to address misperceptions of these children as "deviant" and as not entitled to the same feelings and needs as their typical peers
- Increased awareness of how adults contributed to "problem behaviors"
- Most importantly, adults' realization of the numerous ways we failed to do "our job"

This does not mean children with ASD do not have any responsibility for their behavior. In fact, with increased instructional and motivational programming, that responsibility increases.

Unfortunately, when it comes to social/sexual behavior or relationships, children with ASD are often not seen as entitled to the same opportunities as their peers. In part, this biased perspective is due to viewing adolescents with ASD as socially incompetent "children," regardless of their age, capability, or developmental level. Rather than teach the appropriate behavior, the desired outcome is to squelch social/sexual needs and behavior altogether.

The Lessons We Teach

At this point, it should be painfully apparent how *we* sometimes "miss the boat" and, over the course of years, may inadvertently lay the foundation for the development of social/sexual problems in children with ASD:

- Social judgment errors—no awareness or ability to interpret or understand subtle social cues, situations and "rules"
- Utilizing and following the "wrong rules"
- Deficits in social confidence, assertiveness, and self-advocacy
- Inability to identify or access natural supports and resources
- Social isolation—the inability to form peer relationships
- Confusion regarding social boundaries and relationships

Specifically, we sometimes "teach the wrong lessons" and fail to teach critical ones.

The Wrong Lessons We "Teach"

- Dependency on adults to make decisions, and to provide for and accommodate basic needs.
- Passivity and compliance to authority as keys to survival. ("Do what you're told without question, so that you can access desires and rewards.")
- Reliance on adults as "social" substitutes, rendering peer relationships unimportant.
- Contradictory social norms through accommodation and excusing unacceptable behavior. (Yet, somewhat amazingly, we expect our children to know, practice, and adhere to typical standards.)
- Asexuality. ("Sex is bad—don't talk or even think about it. You're a child; sex is not for you! It is certainly not something you should feel and by all means not something you should act upon.")

The Right Lessons We Fail to Teach

- Sources to access for social/sexual education
- Accurate and functional social/sexual knowledge and information
- Requisite, related social concepts and processes
- Personal rights and self-advocacy in general, and in relation to social/sexuality in particular
- How to "read the fine print" (awareness) for understanding, learning, or adhering to social/sexual norms and rules
- Guidelines related to the dynamics of social/sexual relationships, including understanding and navigating these relationships
- Basic discriminations of when and when not to engage in social/sexual responding
- Basic skills necessary for self-protection and reduction of victimization potential

All in all, this lack of information and avoidance leads to an absence of critical skills and knowledge. At best, uncertainty and confusion diminish a child's sense of social/sexual competence or confidence. As a result of *our* teaching (both what we do and what we fail to do), the potential for children with ASD to develop healthy, mutually consensual, and satisfying social/sexual relationships to the extent possible becomes limited. Further, for children with limited capabilities, safety may be compromised. The saddest part is experience shows that, for many children with ASD, it doesn't have to be this way!

Suggestions for Navigating Adolescence: A Traveler's Guide

To suggest a "map" exists that guarantees smooth sailing through adolescence (for any teenager) would be ludicrous. However, when dealing with ASD-affected children, there are obvious mistakes and pitfalls that we can easily avoid. By the same token, some critical considerations can clearly be addressed and prioritized. Suggestions in regard to these considerations have been offered throughout this chapter. Additionally, the following outline can serve as an overarching guide for "navigation" through the tumultuous journey that is adolescence.

Collaboration: You Need a Crew and Can't Do It Alone

Most travel vessels require a crew; likewise, those responsible for an adolescent with ASD must work as a team and in consonance. Socialization and social/sexual needs, as well as related foreseeable hazards, are the responsibility of *all* relevant parties (e.g., parents, school staff, and other professionals) and cannot be sufficiently addressed by any one party. The probability of reaching a desired destination (that is, a positive resolution or outcome) is greatly enhanced by all significant groups and individuals working together. Blaming and pointing fingers is doomed to result in failure. Without a behind-the-scenes crew working together constructively and cooperatively, a child's potential will be precluded and adolescence will be an even more daunting voyage.

Perspective and Effort: Departure, Travel Time, and Destination

There are three important questions pertaining to this area: What's your destination? What's the estimated travel time? When will you depart?

Destination: Determining the destination means envisioning the desired, realistic, long-term outcome. In many ways, adolescence is a period of transition. Where do you want to see the child in 10 years? What's *really* important and relevant to the child's future options and quality of life?

Estimated Travel Time: How long it will take for the child to reach his or her potential destination? How commensurate are his or her skills with that desired outcome? The bigger the gap, the longer the required travel time. Foundations for independent social competence (e.g., understanding, connectedness, responsibility), even when reasonable as goals, won't be acquired in a single day or a single lesson. Work in requisite, foundational, and essential social skills is critical to the comfort, quality, and pace of the journey through adolescence toward adulthood.

Departure: When will you start focusing on important skill areas as priorities? The later you depart, the more time is needed and the less time the child has to close the gap. With each passing day, deficits in essential skills become further compounded—and progressively more difficult to remediate and less likely to be readily learned. The longer you wait to plan/book the excursion, the higher the cost! Delaying the departure by waiting, avoiding, or focusing elsewhere means the child will reach his or her destination in a less timely and more effortful manner (if at all). No matter what the child's age, functioning, or capabilities, the relevant social skills effort can begin today. Ideally, such effort will begin when the child is quite young (i.e., 2 to 5 years of age). But don't be discouraged if the child is older: It's never too late to embark on this expedition. Starting when he or she is 10 years old offers greater opportunity than starting when the child is 15. But starting at age 15 is still better than waiting until he or she is 20 . . .

Bottom Line: Try as you might, you can't shorten a long, hard journey through denial and avoidance. The child's potential future (and it is not unreasonable, while being realistic, to aim high) should serve as a vision to light the way for what you do *now*. Reducing and even avoiding some pitfalls requires digging in and starting as soon as possible. The important lessons begin early and are *not* merely about "sex" or exclusively tied to other adolescent-only issues. No matter what the child's age, there is truly no time for addressing teenage-related social issues like the present.

Picking and Prioritizing Targets: Points of Interest

Once you have identified your destination, are ready for departure, and have a sense of your travel time, what are the points of interest on your trip? This is the time to focus on the competencies that the child needs to enrich and support his or her adolescent social experience to the maximum extent possible (and will be essential for reaching the journey's ultimate destination). It may be of value to consider the following question, no matter what the child's functioning or capabilities: Which skills would be necessary for the child to successfully operate in his or her current social world, to experience its social benefits, and to manage its daily challenges to a greater extent than at the present time? While there may be many skills to be learned, keep in mind that a complicated itinerary requires more time to plan, develop, and execute. Only a select number of targets need to be addressed to begin the journey.

The following is a sample list of potential "points of interest":

- How does the child handle the situation when events don't go as expected or the usual routine is altered?
- Does the child make and express simple decisions (e.g., picking clothes to wear, decorating his or her room, ordering at a restaurant)?
- Does the child adhere to social norms for respecting others (e.g., physical boundaries, personal property)?
- Does the child initiate social contact?
- Does the child understand and practice standards of privacy (e.g., closing the door before he or she undresses, knocking before walking into your bedroom)?
- Does the child reciprocate small favors within the family or see this action as necessary?
- How aware is the child of those in his or her immediate social world?
- How familiar is the child with relevant social categories (e.g., friends, strangers)?
- How does the child spend his or her free (leisure) time as compared to peers?
- Does the child learn from peers? Do peers "rub off" on him or her?
- Does the child demonstrate particular interest in (e.g., gravitate toward, track) a specific peer?
- How many interests does the child have in common with his or her peers?
- How important is independence to the child?

While this list is far from all inclusive, these kinds of skills form the foundation for expanded social experience, successful social navigation, the formation of relationships, and social/sexual competence in adolescence.

There will be many potential social targets. Chances are, you'll need to decide which points of interests are "must see" and "must do" attractions. One must decide which wayside stops are essential to adolescent success and which are essential and/or foundational to achieving the long-term goals.

Many other domains (including academics) will inevitably present as potential areas of educational or interventional effort. Think about these possibilities from the following perspectives:

When the child is 25, will it matter:

- What grade he or she got on his or her spelling test?
- How much U.S. history he or she learned?
- Whether the child knows a circle from an eclipse, or a wigwam from a tee-pee?

When the child is 25, how will he or she:

- Understand "privacy," if he or she is going to the bathroom with the door open now?
- Share common peer interests, if his or her primary pastime is watching *Thomas the Train*?
- Consider the needs or feelings of others, if everyone continues catering to the child's needs and feelings?
- Make responsible decisions about sexual behavior, if a parent is still deciding which clothes the child wears?
- Connect or engage with people, if he or she currently doesn't initiate social contact with others, is unaware of their presence, or spends all of his or her leisure time on a computer?
- Handle things when a friend changes the plan, if he or she presently rigidly adheres to routines?

Social targets should be meaningful in that they will bring genuine social benefit to the child in everyday life. Points of interest that merely represent illusions (i.e., that create the appearance of social behavior, but are insubstantial or nonfunctional) need not be included in the travel itinerary.

Social goals should also be relevant to the world in which the adolescent lives. The styles, manner, and culture of the immediate teenage environment need to realistically be taken into consideration. That is not to say the goals and expectations for the adolescent with ASD should be identical to those of typical children. Certainly, points of interest need to realistic, achievable, and most likely modified (climbing Mount Everest would not likely be on the first trip's agenda). At the same time, it is important not to start out by underestimating the child's capabilities or to waste time and energy contemplating reasons he or she can't accomplish social milestones. In general, establish social/behavioral expectations that approximate social norms (as much as possible). Then break things down and shape the next small step until, only after all reasonable effort, the child proves you wrong.

Tactics, Strategies, and Methods: Plotting and Steering the Course

The question now becomes, given the destination, departure, and crucial points of interests, how will you get from here to there?

Any voyage will not result in successful destination attainment without careful charting and an established travel protocol. Instilling social competencies in an adolescent with ASD requires systematic teaching and structured motivational programming. Such children do not assimilate social skills through osmosis! Teaching techniques suitable for such purposes with adolescents include as Discrete Trial Teaching[65] and Teaching Interactions (see Chapter 2). Targets need to be broken down into readily teachable lessons (see Chapter 7). Dignifying and age-fitting motivation arrangements (e.g., self-management systems, contingency contracts) should be developed and employed when possible. And, of course, provisions are critical on any expedition. Incentives that are age appropriate, yet meaningful for the child will be critical until work can fade to natural consequences. A motivated crew (even an oppositional teenage one) will not mutiny when adequate provisions and proper incentives are provided.

Even with the best of planning, it is essential to be prepared for the unexpected, as oftentimes this journey requires navigating uncharted territory.

Don't always coddle and protect your child from the real world! Look forward to and even celebrate age-typical and sometimes unanticipated challenges (teasing, bullying, peer attempts to exploit the child). Your natural instinct may be to protect and make the "problem" go away by intervening on the child's behalf. But don't lose sight of the ultimate destination: In the real world, the child will be confronted with far worse than the "jerk" picking on him or her at nutrition or lunch. Attempt, when possible, to treat these instances as real-life teachable moments. In essence, don't always steer the ship for the child; when possible, use the opportunity to teach the child how to steer! Further, when they are available, sometimes allow for the occurrence of natural outcomes and contingencies. Of course, there are many times when children must be protected from the natural results of their choices, behaviors, or deficits. On some occasions, however, the experiencing of mild natural consequences can have powerful motivational and lesson-instilling effects (and preclude the occurrence of later, more devastating natural outcomes).

Conversely, don't always wait for problems to arise before teaching. Create learning opportunities and foster age-typical experiences. Promoting learning in artificial arrangements may be necessary until the ship is ready for open waters. This often allows for systematic, progressive social skills development.

Seize opportunities to address the subject, as opposed to running from them. If sexually charged questions, sexually naïve statements, or even slang/street comments are made (e.g. "Can I sleep with Mary?", "Can I touch those [breasts]?") try not to over-react, judge (e.g.. "Good boys/girls don't talk about that"), age the response downward (e.g., provide infantile terms and answers), lie (e.g., "Only married people can make babies"), dismiss it, or avoid the event entirely. Instead, use the opportunity to teach and establish contexts and boundaries for such discussions (e.g., timing, place, style, audience, to neutrally and gently gain information (e.g., "Why do you ask?" or "Where did you hear that?"), and to educate regarding facts and content (e.g., "That word means . . ."). The opportunity can also be used to encourage the child to return to you and to come forward with similar questions, thoughts, or confusion in the future. This kind of response may be difficult with social/sexual issues. But remember—an ounce of prevention . . .

> **Bottom Line:** A journey will not occur without planning and a travel method and means. The adolescent with ASD will not develop meaningful social skills merely through hope, guidance, and exposure to typical peers. Further, perhaps it might be easier and more comfortable to avoid discussing or addressing some social/sexual subjects, but consider that if the child is not brought to the issue, it may very well come to him or her. What might the learning experience then be?

Evaluation, Analysis, and Modification: Course Corrections—Travel and Weather Conditions

You may be on course, with the trip proceeding as planned, when you suddenly encounter untoward elements or circumstances that are out of your control. No one could have sufficiently predicted there would be a pile-up on the interstate or turbulence in the air or a perfect storm out at sea. It could turn out that the vessel wasn't adequately designed or engineered to meet the particular conditions encountered.

Even with the best planning possible, you can never predict all the challenges that will be faced and how the child will actually handle all situations. Ultimately, all factors faced in the real social world cannot be anticipated; thus more accurate prognosis of a program's potential for success comes with actual implementation. Throughout the journey, it's important to evaluate the rate of progress in relation to your goals and anticipated timeline, the specific course, and the crew's navigation of the route. It is highly likely that you will need to change course, adjust expectations, amend priorities, and modify methods at some juncture.

Some examples of potential complications follow:

- It becomes apparent that there are areas of weakness (social deficits) that the child is either incapable of or currently ill equipped to overcome.
- The target area proves to be less meaningful or functional than originally thought.
- A shift in the social landscape occurs.
- New, more urgent social priorities arise.
- The social goal is achievable, but not with the current program.
- The current program is appropriate, but is not being implemented as designed.
- The lesson needs to be broken down into smaller, learnable steps.
- The program is recognized as being overly ambitious.
- The program expects or demands too little from the child.

Ongoing assessment of the program, even in informal fashion, is necessary to evaluate the program and its effectiveness. When the unanticipated becomes apparent, the crew (team) makes adjustments to programmatic elements as well as to targets, priorities, and the ultimate objectives. Given the nature of any adventure and the diverse applied interventional programs implemented in the real world, this is the hallmark of resourceful and artful navigation.

Generalization and Independence: Soundness of the Vessel/Arriving at the Destination

To eventually safely arrive at its home port, in addition to taking into account all of the previously mentioned considerations, the vessel must be sea worthy and sound. All work in the social area done with a child becomes unsound when programming does not result in independent application of skills in the natural social environment. Underlying all work should be purposeful effort focused on promoting the independence (both general and specific to particular skills) of the adolescent and the utilization of skills in everyday life.

This understanding may be relevant in such areas as the following:

- Selection and use of prompts
- Focus on meaningful skills
- Emphasis on developing social learning abilities
- Embedding of instruction in natural contexts
- Specific generalization programming

When the overarching emphasis is on independence, then true social skills performance has occurred. Additionally, promotion of independence brings a child closer to the core of mainstream adolescence in a general sense, given that independent growth is a central element of this developmental stage. Further, if independence is fostered in an overall sense during adolescence, along with competency and responsibility, then essential preparation for adulthood is also occurring. When work on independent skill performance is paired with transfer of skills to everyday life (and with recognition of the capabilities and potential of the particular child), then the purpose of the journey is realized and the child's social destination begins to appear on the horizon.

Challenging Is Not the Same as Impossible

Adolescence is a difficult period of life that serves as a transition to and preparation for the rest of life. Compounding this issue is the fact that many lessons are easier to teach and some behaviors can be more readily instilled earlier in life.

At the same time, adolescence is a period of remarkable growth and change for all children. In fact, some needs and opportunities do not even present themselves until adolescence. Truly, adolescence is a period of unparallel learning—and there is no reason why this cannot be true for a teenager with ASD.

With strong and solid instructional and programmatic efforts, many adolescents with ASD can independently acquire meaningful social skills, from basic to advanced. Ultimately, these youths can successfully contribute to and draw from their adolescent social world as well as handle its incumbent challenges.

While families and professionals often see this period of development as a time for slowing down interventional efforts (early intervention being all the rage), we would argue for the opposite approach. As noted throughout this chapter, a strong argument can be made for sprinting, in the social skills development sense, to the next phase of life. In a real sense, that next phase is only the beginning.

5

True Friendships

Mitchell Taubman, Jon Rafuse, Justin Leaf, and Ron Leaf

Ask parents' raising a child with autism spectrum disorder (ASD) what their highest hopes are for their son or daughter, and you will often hear the same refrain: Having meaningful friendships and being truly happy. This chapter is designed to help parents and professionals understand what qualifies as a true friendship for a person with ASD as well as provide some guidance on how such relationships can be built.

It is certainly our experience that much is unclear when it comes to the topic of friendships for persons with ASD. This confusion occurs not only in regard to what it takes to establish such relationships, but even as to what truly makes a friendship a friendship. To begin, then, it makes sense to develop a working definition of what constitutes a true friendship—and what does not.

What Makes a Friendship?

If you took a poll on what a friend is, you would likely get a variety of answers: "Someone you like to spend time with," "Someone to talk to," "Someone who is there for you," "Someone you admire," "Someone who respects you for who you are," "A person you look forward to seeing," "Someone who makes you laugh," "A person you can trust," "Someone who knows what I am thinking without asking." In actuality, these factors or qualities may or may not be displayed by the parties involved in a friendship, yet such a relationship may still exist. At some level, a friendship may exist just because the parties involved have defined it as a friendship. A key, however, is that both parties must do so for it truly to be so; that is, for the friendship to be true and authentic, the persons involved must agree that their relationship is, indeed, a friendship.

It is reasonable to think that some level of reciprocity (things being shared, done, felt, or shown by both sides) is a necessary ingredient for friendship. Reciprocity or mutuality would appear to be an important ingredient in other ways as well. This has to do not only with the give and take within the relationship, but also with the equality or parity of the relationship itself. For example, if within the relationship one party has great authority over the other, or if one is a caretaker for the other, then "friendship" may not be the appropriate label for the association.

Writers and researchers who have focused on the subject have consistently noted the importance of reciprocity in true friendships.[19, 102, 124]

This consideration has special implications for friendships for persons with ASD. All too often individuals with ASD may have associations with peers that are not reciprocal, yet are referred to as friendships. Examples would be when peers treat the child parentally, when they are trained as junior therapists, or when they are consistently directed to spend time with and interact with the child with ASD. True friendships, by comparison, are genuinely reciprocal relationships, where the parties are not together just because adults have made it happen. True friendships exist when both parties are at similar positions in the relationship, when they treat each other similarly, and both parties have similar desires to be with each other.

Other factors that have been identified as important parts of friendships include common interests and activities; consistent contact; overlapping or shared enjoyment, experiences, or knowledge; pleasant regard; emotional support; physical attraction; commitment; trust; desire for and anticipation of contact; and opportunity for enhanced experience or personal growth.[5, 28, 30, 46, 52, 85, 129]. It would seem, then, that a genuine and quality friendship for a person with ASD would likely contain at least some of these elements.

Are Friendships Important?

Research has shown that a lack of friendships can have serious effects on the functioning and well-being of child, including one with ASD. Children who are able to build and maintain friendships do better in school,[59] have positive perceptions of school,[44] have higher self-esteem,[59] have better social cognitive skills, and have reduced stress levels[69] compared to those children who do not have friendships. Research has also shown that those children who do not have friendships do worse in academics,[59] have more social anxiety,[38] are lonelier than children who have friends,[10] and stand a greater risk of committing or attempting to commit suicide[42] than those children who have friends.

Children with ASD have difficulty in establishing and maintaining quality friendships. In one study, Bauminger and Sulamn compared mothers' perceptions of friendships for 14 typically developing children and 14 children with ASD.[11] Results showed that children with ASD did have some friends, though these friendships usually developed with the help of the children's parents. This study revealed the difficulty children with ASD have in establishing friendships, according to the reports of parents. In prior research, Bauminger and Kasari found that when children with ASD had friends, the relationships were fewer and were of poorer friendship quality (e.g., lack of communication, play, and social support) than the relationships forged by typically developing children. In addition, children with ASD were lonelier than typically developing children.[10] Stewart and colleagues conducted an analysis on the prevalence rate of depression for children diagnosed with ASD[115]; the results showed that 4% to 38% of children with ASD suffer from depressive symptoms.

Given this body of work, as well as common sense, it would seem that helping persons with ASD develop and maintain friendships would be very worthwhile. Why, then, is such work so limited and rare? Several reasons explain this phenomenon. First, more than one party is involved in a friendship. Second, social skills contribute to the establishment and maintenance of friendships. On the one hand, social skills and social relationships are not the same thing. We all know of individuals who appear to have extremely limited social ability, yet somehow manage to find each other. On the other hand, the impact of social skills on friendships is often great. The difficulty in addressing social behavior is noted elsewhere in this book (see the Introduction and Chapter 8) and the amount of hard work involved is certainly clear. Ultimately, these factors make effort in the friendship area for persons with ASD all the more challenging. Finally, much remains unknown about the essential ingredients for the chemical reaction that produces friendship and attraction. For this reason, much of the effort directed at friendship development within the field of ASD treatment emphasizes unclear and almost magical processes as the core of the approach. Some efforts just try to create exposure and opportunity, as if somehow friendships will spring from a child with ASD just being around another child. In other cases, friendship development becomes a matter of hope and wishes.

What is needed is effort that does not leave friendship development to chance or magic. Such an approach would also need to be mindful of the delicate essence of human bonding—otherwise, just friendship actions are produced, instead of the authentic and quality relationships that are truly desired.

A Contemporary ABA Approach to Friendship Development

Importance of Social Skills

A large portion of the ways and means to build friendships is covered in other parts of this book. Social skills are contained in the taxonomy and curriculum (see Chapter 8 and the Curriculum section), and methods for building them (see the discussion of Teaching Interactions in Chapter 2 and social skills groups in Chapter 3) are also described. Working in these areas will certainly help children with ASD learn to build and maintain friendships.[64]

Of special importance are the skills contained in the "Social Relatedness" section of the social skills taxonomy. These skills connect a person to another; they draw someone toward a social relationship and promote the work necessary to develop and maintain that relationship. Perhaps more importantly, such skills often represent styles and characteristics in a person that would be attractive to another—in other words, the qualities that produce reciprocity and bonding.

Take, for example, the program "Building of Social Interest and Desire" (a full description is contained within the *Social Relatedness* section of the Social Skills Curriculum in this book). With growth in these areas, not only is the person with ASD likely to seek and initiate interactions with others, it is also probable that he or she is will develop a desire and need for social connection. With such desire, the person is likely to work at making relationships satisfying and successful. Add to that the skill area of empathy (also part of the "Social Relatedness" section of the taxonomy): If a person shows empathy, then a friend is likely to find the person appealing and be committed to the friendship.

The building of social skills, especially those that enhance the give and take and enrichment of a relationship, is highly likely to enhance friendships. At the same time, other efforts and considerations are also important to the development of true friendships.

Finding Good Matches

The identification of potential candidates for friendships is often an initial step undertaken by a parent or professional. This effort does not merely focus on finding any child who can serve as a friend; rather, it means attempting to identify and match children who will mutually benefit from a relationship. This might mean finding children of similar temperament, manner, and interests, or it might mean finding matches where children will complement each other. It may mean looking at typically developing children or searching for prospects among special needs peers. The key is that the other children identified are good candidates for a reciprocal, mutually beneficial relationship.

Facilitating the Process

If opportunities for social contact and experiences can be arranged (for example, through play dates, as discussed later in this chapter), the parent or professional must serve an important role—as facilitator. The facilitator contributes to the relationship-building process in important ways. At the same time, the facilitator must be mindful of not being over-involved or attempting to control what will need to be an independently developing (between the two children involved) process.

In addition to finding a good match, the facilitator may need to arrange things in a number of ways. Obviously, the facilitator may need to plan and schedule events. He or she may need to make sure that events are appealing, and that when possible the activities emphasize the benefits of the presence of each party to the other. For example, the facilitator may need to create special experiences that are not otherwise available to the children involved, except for their times with each other. The facilitator will need to carefully craft common time that benefits from the parties' similarities as well as highlights how their differences can enhance the experience. Interactive, cooperative, and competitive activities need to be developed to ensure that play dates involve shared and connection-promoting experiences. Finally, the parent or professional will need to create opportunities that allow for a balance of the fresh and novel along with the repeated and familiar. Such a balance is necessary for the common experiences and the routines of friendship to develop. All of this will serve as the foundation for the establishment of the friendship, be facilitative of the process, and underscore the unique and special nature of the relationship.

Facilitation, Not Control

Of even greater importance, however, is the care that must be taken in performing the facilitator role. It is easy, when serving in this role, to become overly involved in the moments, episodes, and interactions of the friendship activities. This is especially true if the facilitator's role is instructive—that is, if the facilitator is attempting to teach or generalize social skills during the social activities in addition to building friendships. When the priority is friendship, the facilitator must be careful not to become over-involved in the moment, because doing so alters, and may stifle, the process of friendship development. The facilitator's role is to set things in motion and at times guide the parties, but not to over-control or intrude. The facilitator may need to restrain himself or herself in the name of the independent development and evolution of the friendship. He or she may need to respect that the developing friendship is different than the one originally imagined, especially when the relationship is clearly appealing to children and being independently designed by them.

To help make this process unfold, it may be necessary for the facilitator to establish that certain events are friendship opportunities whereas others are designated for skills development, thereby helping the facilitator sort out his or her roles. Of course, this does not mean that the facilitator has no programmatic role and that the children should be left to their own devices. It is not realistic to believe that one simply needs to create social occasions and then friendships for persons with ASD will somehow magically develop. As noted earlier, the facilitator not only creates the opportunity, but also infuses it with elements designed to enhance friendship development. Hence the facilitator acts throughout (e.g., guiding or promoting the process, prompting and prompt fading for social skill performance, course correcting, emphasizing the friendship-building elements). Nevertheless, when friendship development is the objective, the facilitator should set the table, put things in motion, prime the pump, establish and enforce guidelines, assist a little when indicated, and then get out of the way.

A Few Words about Playmates and Play Dates

Over the years, we have observed many play dates (get-togethers with another child or children to provide social opportunities) for children with ASD. Most of them involve preplanned activities and parents or professionals facilitating the child with ASD to interact or socialize with the playmate. The general idea is that being in the presence of a peer, in a social situation, is somehow sufficient to produce positive outcomes for a child with ASD. Additionally, a lot of assistance, guidance, facilitation (prompts that are not faded), and herding are usually involved. In reality, over time, this approach just does not seem to accomplish much. This outcome should not comes as a surprise because systematic programming, as opposed to mere exposure and guidance, is necessary to build independent social skills and real friendships with children with ASD.[91]

In general, the objectives of play dates most often involve trying to build one or more of the following:

- Social tolerance
- Social awareness
- Social interest
- Social skills
- Friendship

Although this is not often the case, the objectives of the play date should determine much of the event. Objectives should guide:

- The nature of the activities
- The targets for the child with ASD
- The type of programming (motivational and instructional) that occurs
- The playmate characteristics

Let's look at each of the objectives identified previously and consider how a play date should be designed around that purpose.

Tolerance

Tolerance is the objective when the play date has been scheduled so that the child with ASD can become comfortable around peers. This is the only case where exposure is really enough. Gradual, systematic exposure to peers can help a child with ASD tolerate the presence of a peer. It will not necessarily result in awareness and interest, but it can reduce intolerance, rejection, and withdrawal. With this objective in mind, the facilitator should decide how many children will be involved; for example, play dates may start with one child at a distance, then with closer proximity, and so on, until it eventually includes several children playing around the target child. Also, the manner and behavior of the playmate should be considered; for example, a more passive child may be sought at the beginning, and more lively children blended into the mix as greater tolerance develops.

Awareness

The objective of awareness involves the child with ASD noticing the presence of peers as well as reading the cues and signals they send. Activities should be chosen that make the peers as noticeable as possible and involve positive interactions (or intrusions) with the child with ASD. Activities should also be selected that allow for programming in observational learning and observational awareness[65] and the reading of social cues (see the Curriculum section in this book). Such activities would involve discrete behaviors and verbalizations that the target child could easily (given his or her capability) observe, copy, and discriminate. Peers involved in play dates with social awareness objectives should not be so capable that the child with ASD could not possibly notice or grasp their actions. With success, modeled behavior can gradually become more sophisticated and complex.

Interest

The interest objective represents a more ambitious objective than the awareness goal. Interest is shown when a child tracks the actions of a peer, gravitates toward him or her, anticipates his or her arrival, is excited upon his or her appearance, or is noticeably affected by his or her departure. The objective also involves the building of social desire.

Activities and materials during such play dates should be fun and compelling. They should allow for social temptations, cooperation, competition, and programming designed to show how the presence of peers can enhance activities and tasks (see the "Peer Social Interest/Engagement" program in the Curriculum section of this book). Peers who are willing and able to engage in such activities should be included in these play dates.

Social Skills

For some play dates, the primary purpose is the learning of specific social skills (see Chapter 8 and the Curriculum section of this book). Systematic teaching is often embedded in such play dates. At least at the beginning, planned activities that allow for such teaching are scheduled. Over time, less structure is included so learned skills can transfer to naturally occurring situations. Peers with similar skills (and needs) allow for group teaching. Peers with higher capabilities (but not so high that they are not accessible) allow for good modeling and observational learning.

Friendships

When the objective of a play date is the building of friendships, then the considerations discussed in the preceding sections guide the play date experience. That is, prerequisite skills should be in place, good peer matches (for possible friendships) should be made, the friendship development process should be guided as necessary, and care should be taken to fade facilitation and allow, as much as possible, the friendship development process to unfold naturally.

Of course, a play date may include more than one of these objectives at the same time (although meeting a single objective may sometimes be the case). The point is that the objective should be clear and the purpose or multiple purposes of the play date should then guide the content and nature of the event.

How Do I Know When It Is a True Friendship?

This question returns us to our original discussion. *Reciprocity* is certainly an important ingredient, including that the relationship is even and balanced. At the same time, other indicators may be useful in answering this question as it relates to a child with ASD:

- *Preference:* Does the child prefer being with and interacting with the peer as compared to other children or to solo activities?
- *Gravitation:* In a open, unstructured social situation, does the child independently seek out or otherwise move toward proximity with the peer?
- *Spontaneous Initiation:* Does the child independently request or otherwise indicate a desire for contact or opportunities for interaction with the peer (e.g., does the child ask for play dates)?
- *Anticipation:* Does the child actually look forward to play dates or other contact with the peer? Does the student bring it up in conversation before it happens, and exhibit excitement or joy when thinking about it or talking about it?
- *Uniqueness:* Does the relationship appear to have its own special elements, routines, activities, and personality, distinct from other relationships?

A Final Note

Like much in this book, the efforts described in this chapter are designed to promote an outcome in a planned and sometimes structured way, while preserving the essence of that desired outcome. This balancing act is especially tricky when it comes to the delicate, hard-to-capture, and highly varied phenomena of friendships. Friendships for students with ASD are unlikely to develop suddenly, without prior social skills development and much facilitative work. At the same time, care and—dare we say—artfulness are necessary to promote and allow for the growth of authentic and special relationships known as friendships. Such effort turns out to be a bit of a tight-rope walk, but one that is both very doable and deeply important.

6

Assessment of Social Skills in ASD: A User's Guide

B. J. Freeman

Autism spectrum disorder (ASD) comprises a group of disorders in which the innate ability to engage in mutually satisfying complex social interactions does not exist. Kanner, in his original description of autism, proposed that it was a congenital disorder.[53] He contrasted the lack of social interest (autism) with the marked predisposition of typically developing children to engage in reciprocal interactions. Later research has clearly shown that social interest is present at birth in typically developing infants. Research over the past few years has also suggested that ASD represents a set of neurodevelopmental disorders that result in significant social communication deficits and a restricted range of interest. However, attempts to define the precise nature of these social deficits have been limited by the complexity of the expression of ASD.

This chapter provides information on testing and assessment of social skills as relevant to individuals with ASD. Reviews of a number of tests and other pertinent assessment information are furnished. Information is generally categorized based on the objectives of the assessment. A table is also provided to summarize information on available tests, grouped by and with additional details regarding assessment purpose. The material offered is intended to help users make informed and objective-driven decisions when selecting instruments and developing comprehensive assessment plans.

Social Skill Deficits in ASD

While problems in social skills development are the hallmark of ASD, standardized measurement of such skills has been problematic. Few assessment tools exist specific to ASD that measure both deficits and "social competence." The majority of studies have focused on the various components of social skills and the ways that they may be affected in ASD—for example, joint attention, Theory of Mind, executive functioning. While identifying these deficits is important, their identification alone provides minimal information for designing an appropriate treatment program and teaching of social competence.

Persons with ASD are often said to have social cognitive deficits that result in the failure to develop appropriate social skills. A number of theories have been developed to explain these deficits:

- Central Coherence Theory[32,40]: The majority of persons with ASD have difficulty learning in "chunks" and prefer to attend to detail.
- Executive Dysfunction[89,103]: Results in difficulty organizing tasks for a desired outcome.
- Theory of Mind (ToM)[6]: Persons with ASD have difficulty taking the perspective of other people.

In addition to behavioral descriptions of these theories, correlates of brain functioning have been identified.[99] While identifying the underlying causes and neurocorrelates of social skills deficits is important, it does not give us information about how a specific individual functions in his or her day-to-day environment.

Klin, Jones, Schultz and Volkmar discuss in detail the problem of social deficits on ASD.[55] They point out that the discrepancy between what persons with ASD can do on very structured tasks of social reasoning and how they function on a day-to-day basis represents one of the most "intriguing puzzles" in the field. This dilemma—ability to solve problems verbally, but inability to spontaneously apply skills in the natural environment—has created the difficulties in measuring social skills. Klin and colleagues also point out that there has been little research defining the magnitude of this discrepancy. To date, the most frequently used measure has been the social domain on the *Vineland Adaptive Behavior Scales*.[114] However, this norm-referenced scale provides little information as to which skills need to be specifically taught.

To further complicate matters, emphasis in social skills research has been on treatment rather than assessment. Reichow and Volkmar reviewed the scientific literature on social skills treatment.[99] One of the major problems they found is a lack of proper assessment tools that would allow measurement of meaningful change in social skills in the natural environment.

Issues in Measurement of Social Communication Skills

Definitions of social skills vary from person to person and from situation to situation. Some researchers have hypothesized that it makes no sense to separate social skills from communication skills and that both should be measured together.[73, 128] Others, mostly behaviorists, point out that social and communications skills can and should be assessed separately and independently. The latter position is supported by the fact that measurement of social skills has lagged significantly behind measurement of communication skills. There is a large literature on language and communication assessment, and psychometric tests have been developed to measure these skills. Social skills, by their very nature, are very heterogeneous and always in flux. How a specific skill is expressed is dynamic and influenced by a number of variables at any one point in time. How a skill is exhibited may vary significantly within the same person in different situations. How a person responds changes the entire nature of the interaction.

Wetherby and Waters reviewed the psychometric issues in measurement of social communication (the same issues occur in measurement of social skills)[128]. They include how the information is gathered; which social communication behaviors are measured; whether the items on the scale are homogeneous; whether the child's behavior is judged similarly by different raters; how stable the measure is from test to retest; whether the measure captures growth/change in this construct; whether the measure has an empirical association with some criterion measure; how the measure differentiates ASD from other disorders; and whether the measure actually measures the construct it purports to measure. Few, if any, measures of social skills meet all of these criteria.

While a large body of literature focuses on measurement of social skills in typically developing children, few, if any, studies have addressed assessment in ASD. Attempts to measure social deficits in ASD fall into three categories: (1) screening instruments; (2) diagnostic measures; and (3) interactive measures. Within each of these areas, assessment tools can be classified into norm-referenced assessments and environmental assessments. In norm-referenced approaches, the aim is to identify skills used by peers who are socially competent and to determine how the person with ASD compares. In environment-based assessments, the goal is to identify discrepancies between what is required in a particular social situation and the behavior shown by the person with ASD.[16]

The following sections provide information on tests and assessments, based on a user's potential objectives. Table 6.1 summarizes current available social skills assessment tools.

Screening Tools

Screening tools aim to identify social behaviors that may indicate a diagnosis of ASD and require further assessments. A number of screening instruments of this type are being developed. The majority focus on the first two years of life and are not useful for older children.

The *Autism Observation Scale for Infants* (AOSI)[18] is an observational measure designed to detect signs of ASD in infants 6 to 18 months of age. After a brief interaction, the examiner completes a checklist for 18 risk markers for ASD, including visual attention, disengagement, coordination of eye gaze with action, imitation, affect, behavioral reactivity, social communication and sensory-motor behaviors.

The *First Year Inventory* (FYI)[100] is a questionnaire administered to caregivers to identify 12-month-old children at risk for atypical development in general and ASD in particular. A 63-item checklist rates the child in two areas—social and communication.

The *Early Screening for Autistic Traits* (ESAT) questionnaire[121] is a two-stage, 14-item population screener for 14- to 15-month-old children. In studies of this tool, four items were identified as having good discriminability for ASD: readability of emotions, reaction to sensory stimuli, and two play behaviors—interest in different toys and varied play. A large number of false positives were found in the initial sample. This instrument should be used with caution, but it points out the complexity inherent in measurement of social behavior.

Both the full *Communication and Symbolic Behavior Scales* (CSBS)[127] and its shorter version are standardized tools for assessing social, communication, and play behaviors in 14- to 24-month-old children. Five pivotal social skills were detected in studies of this assessment tool: communicative intent, conventional behaviors, representation, social referencing, and rate of communication.

TABLE 1: SOCIAL SKILLS RATING SCALES

I. SCREENING TOOLS	PURPOSE:	FORM:	SCORES / SOCIAL BEHAVIORS MEASURED:
Autism Observational Scale for Infants (AOSI) (Bryson, McDermott et al, 2000)	Infant screening, ages 6–18 months	Observational checklist of 18 behaviors	Overall score/Visual attention, coordination of eye gaze with action, imitation, affect, behavioral reactivity, social-communication & sensory-motor behaviors.
First Year Inventory (FYI) (Reznick, Baranek et al, 2007)	Identifies atypical behaviors at 12 months	63-item questionnaire	Overall score/Social orienting, receptive communication, social affective engagement, imitation and expressive communication.
Early Screening for Autistic Traits Questionnaire (ESAT) (Swinkels et al, 2006)	Infant screener , ages 14- to 15-months	14-item questionnaire	Overall score/Readability of emotions, reaction to sensory stimuli, interest in different toys and varied play.
Communication and Symbolic Behavior Scales (CSBS) (Wetherby & Prizant, 1993)	Standardized assessment ages 12- to 24-months	Three-measure Infant-Toddler checklist; 14-item screening questionnaire; semi-structured observation	Three composite scores/Social (emotion, eye gaze, communication), Speech (sounds, words), Symbolic (understanding, object use).
Communication and Symbolic Behavior Scales–Developmental Profile (CSBS-DP) (Wetherby & Prizant, 2002)	(Shorter version of CSBS)		
Checklist for Infants and Toddlers (CHAT) (Baron-Cohen, Allen & Gillberg, 1992)	Screener for 18-month-olds at risk for ASD.	14-item observational checklist	Overall score/Protodeclarative pointing, gaze monitoring and pretend play.
Modified Checklist for Infants and Toddlers (M-CHAT) (Robbins, Fein, Bartons & Green, 2001)	Screener for 18-month-olds at risk for ASD.	Parent interview checklist	Overall score/Measures 6 critical items for ASD: interest in other children; pointing with index finger; bringing objects to show parents; imitating; response to name; following a point.
Screening Tool for Autism in Two-Year-Olds (STAT) (Stone & Ousley, 1997)	Differentiates ASD from other developmental disorders, ages 24- to 35-months	Observational play-based interaction.	Overall score/Measures 12 behaviors in 4 social-communication domains: play, requesting, directing attention, motor imitation
Early Social Communication Scales (ESCS) (Mundy, Hogan & Doehring, 1996)	Research-based procedure assesses response to non-verbal communication in 6- to 30-month-olds.	20-minute structured observation.	Frequency scores in 5 areas/ Responding to social interaction; initiating & response; joint attention; responding to joint attention; initiating requests.
II. SCREENING DIAGNOSTIC SCALES	PURPOSE:	FORM:	SCORES / SOCIAL BEHAVIORS MEASURED:
Childhood Autism Rating Scale, Second Edition (CARS2) Schopler, Van Bourgondien, Wellman & Love (2010)	Screener for diagnosis of ASD ages 2+ years	15-item questionnaire and observation	Total Score/Includes items on relating to people

Autism Screening Instrument for Educational Planning - Third Edition (ASIEP-3) Krug, Arick & Almond (2008)	Standardized diagnostic screener, ages 2–13 years	Checklist and observation	Subtest scores in 5 areas/Autism behavior checklist, sample of vocal behavior, interaction assessment, educational assessment, prognosis of learning rate
PDD Behavior Inventory (PDDBI) Cohen & Sudhalter (2005)	Standardized diagnostic screener, ages 1.6 to 12.5 years.	Parent & teacher rating forms	Standardized domain score & 5 composite scores: communication, reciprocal social interaction, ritualistic activities, learning skills
Gilliam Autism Rating Scale – Second Edition (GARS-2) Gilliam (2006)	Standardized diagnostic screener ages 3–22	Rating form	Overall score/Scores in stereotypical behavior, communication, social interaction
Autism Spectrum Rating Scales (ASRS) Goldstein & Naglieri (2008)	Norm-referenced assessment, ages 2–5 years and 6–18 years	15-item form in 2 age groups, parent & teacher forms	Total score/Peer socialization, adult socialization, social-emotional reciprocity, atypical language, stereotypy, behavioral rigidity, sensory sensitivity, attention/self-regulation
Social Communication Questionnaire (SCQ) Rutter, Bailey & Lord (2003)	Diagnostic screener, 4+ years for ASD	40-item checklist based on ADI-R	Total score/Two algorithms: Lifetime & Current
III. ASPERGER'S SCALES	**PURPOSE:**	**FORM:**	**SCORES / SOCIAL BEHAVIORS MEASURED:**
Gilliam Asperger's Disorder Scale (GADS) Gilliam (2001)	Standardized diagnostic screener, 3–22 years	Rating scale	Overall score & 4 subscale scores/ Social interaction, restricted patterns of behavior, cognitive patterns, pragmatic skills
Asperger's Syndrome Diagnostic Scale (ASDS) Myles, Bock & Simpson (2000)	Standardized diagnostic screener, 5–18 years	50-item yes/no checklist	Total score/Cognitive, maladaptive, language, social, sensorimotor
Krugs Asperger's Disorder Index (KADI) Krug & Arick (2002)	Standardized diagnostic screener, 6–21 years	Rating scale	Overall score
Childhood Asperger's Syndrome Test (CAST) Scott, Baron-Cohen, et al (2002)	Diagnostic screener	37-item checklist	Overall score
Asperger's Syndrome Screening Questions (ASSQ) Ehlers, Gillberg & Wing (1999)	Diagnostic screener for school-aged children	Checklist	Overall score
IV. BROADER PHENOTYPE ASSESSMENTS	**PURPOSE:**	**FORM:**	**SCORES / SOCIAL BEHAVIORS MEASURED:**
Autism Spectrum Quotient (AQ) Baron-Cohen, et al (2001)	Self-administered screener, adults with normal intelligence	Questionnaire	Total score/Autistic traits in 5 areas: Social skills, attention switching, attention to detail, communication, imagination

TABLE 1: SOCIAL SKILLS RATING SCALES *(continued)*

Broader Phenotype Autism Symptom Scale (BPASS) Dawson, et al (2007)	Assesses autism-related traits in children & adults	Interview & observation	Total score/Social motivation, social expressiveness, conversational skills, restricted/repetitive behaviors
Friendship Questionnaire(FQ) Baron-Cohen & Wheelwright (2003)	Self-report	Questionnaire	Overall score/Measures individual's ability to enjoy close, empathetic, supportive friendship, interest in interacting with others.
Empathy Questionnaire (EQ) Baron-Cohen & Wheelwright (2004)	Self-report	60-Item Questionnaire	Total or overall empathy score
V. ADAPTIVE BEHAVIOR RATING SCALES	**PURPOSE:**	**FORM:**	**SCORES / SOCIAL BEHAVIORS MEASURED:**
Vineland Adaptive Behavior Scale-Second Edition (Vineland-II) Sparrow, Cicchetti & Balla (2005)	Standardized assessment of social adaptive behavior, ages birth – adult	Parent and teacher rating forms, interview form	Overall & subtest scores/Communication, daily living skills, social, motor skills (under age 7), maladaptive behaviors
Adaptive Behavior Assessment System, Second Edition (ABAS-II) Harrison & Oakland (2003)	Standardized assessment of social adaptive behavior, ages birth – adult	Parent and teacher rating forms, interview form	Overall score/10 subscales: Communication, community use, functional academics, school/home living, health & safety, leisure, self-care, self-direction, social, work
Scales of Independent Behavior-Revised (SIB-R) Bruininks, et al (1996)	Standardized assessment of social adaptive behavior, infants to age 80	Checklist	14 scores/Broad independence in 5 areas: motor, communication (includes social interaction), personal living, community living skills, home/community
VI. DIAGNOSTIC MEASURES	**PURPOSE:**	**FORM:**	**SCORES / SOCIAL BEHAVIORS MEASURED:**
Autism Diagnostic Interview (ADI-R) Rutter, Le Couteour & Lord (2003)	Standardized diagnostic measure, based on DSM-IV	Semi-structured interview	Overall score/Reciprocal social interaction
Autism Diagnostic Observation Scale (ADOS) Lord, Rutter, Di Lavore & Risi (2002)	Standardized diagnostic measure, based on DSM-IV	Standardized semi-structured observational assessment	Overall score/Reciprocal social interaction
Social Responsiveness Scale (SRS) Constantino & Todd (2005)	Measures severity of ASD	65-item rating scale	Total & subscale scores/Social awareness, social cognition, social communication, social motivation, autistic mannerisms
VII. OTHER SOCIAL SKILL SCALES	**PURPOSE:**	**FORM:**	**SCORES / SOCIAL BEHAVIORS MEASURED:**
Matson Evaluation of Social Skills with Youngsters (MESSY) (1983)	Measures social skills, identifies potential problem behaviors in children ages 4–18	62-item self-rating checklist and 64-item teacher rating scale	Overall score/Range of verbal & nonverbal behavior; refers to discrete, observable behaviors

Matson Evaluation of Social Skills for Individuals with Severe Retardation (MESS-IER) (1999)	Measure social skills in adults with severe developmental disabilities	Behavior observation system	Identifies targets for social skills training; 85 skills rated on a 0–3 scale.
Social Skills Improvement System (SSiS) Gresham & Elliott (2008)	Evaluates social skills and problem behaviors	Checklist	Total & subscale scores/7 social skill areas: Communication, Cooperation, Assertion, Responsibility, Empathy, Engagement and Self-Control; and 5 problem behavior areas: Externalizing Problems, Bullying, Hyperactivity/Inattention, Internalizing Problems and Autism Spectrum.

The *Checklist for Autism in Toddlers* (CHAT)[7] is a population-based screening measure developed to identify children at risk for ASD at 18 months of age. The CHAT consists of a 14-item yes/no checklist that is completed by parents and professionals. In studies of this tool, proto-declarative pointing, gaze monitoring, and pretend play were found to have the best predictive value. The *Modified Checklist for Autism in Toddlers* (M-CHAT)[101] added a parent interview to the CHAT. The authors suggested that M-CHAT screening at 24 months improves predictive value of the CHAT administered at 18 months.

The *Screening Tool for Autism in Two-Year-Olds* (STAT)[117] is designed to differentiate young children with ASD from those with other developmental disorders. The STAT is a 20-minute observational measure consisting of 12 items that assess behaviors in four social-communication domains: play, requesting, directing attention, and motor imitation. It has been found to have good sensitivity and specificity.

The *Early Social Communication Scale* (ESCS)[83] is a research-based assessment that measures initiation of and responses to nonverbal communication, including joint attention, social play behaviors, and requesting behaviors. The ESCS is a 20-minute observation of primarily nonverbal children from ages 6 to 30 months. This scale has been found to predict later language development.[82]

While all of these screening devices purport to measure social–communication skills, it is the deficits in the social skills component that have been found to have predictive value in making a diagnosis of ASD. This relationship supports the notion that the core deficit of ASD is social in nature. Furthermore, the development of instruments that adequately reflect this core deficit is a necessary step for teaching social competence.

Screening/Diagnostic Scales

Some other scales can be used for both screening and diagnosis. These tools have often been developed as diagnostic scales but in and of themselves cannot diagnose ASD. All contain a significant social component. The most commonly used are the Childhood Autism Rating Scale and the Gilliam Autism Rating Scale.

The *Childhood Autism Rating Scale* (CARS)[107] has recently been re-normed. It now has two forms, one of which is specifically for higher-functioning children. The CARS involves a combination of observation and interview. It examines how the child's behavior deviates from typical behavior. This rating scale has been especially effective in discriminating between children with ASD and those with severe cognitive defects and in distinguishing mild-to-moderate autism from severe autism. As yet, little research has been conducted on the re-normed CARS.

The *Gilliam Autism Rating Scale* (GARS-2)[35] is a norm-referenced screening instrument designed to assist in screening and diagnosing children with ASD. It is composed of three subscales: stereotypic behavior, communication, and social interaction. An additional section addresses developmental milestones. The GARS has been used as a screening tool, to make a diagnosis, and to measure response to treatment.

The *Social Communication Questionnaire* (SCQ)[104] is designed for use in children older than 4 years of age. This 40-item checklist is based on the *Autism Diagnostic Interview* and has two forms: Current and Lifetime. The SCQ is particularly helpful when evaluating older children and adults. Although it generates an overall score, it does not provide specific communication or social scores.

A number of other diagnostic screening scales are listed in Table 6.1 that are used less frequently. Additionally, Table 6.1 lists a number of diagnostic scales purported to measure deficits reflective of Asperger's disorder, each of which is based on a specific theory of ASD. Some of these instruments yield subdomain scores (e.g., GADS, ASDS), whereas others yield only an overall score. Overall scores are relatively useless in the development of treatment goals: They simply tell us that persons with ASD have social deficits relative to typical persons and, in some instances. may be used to show change over time.

Gamliel and Yirmiya also reviewed rating scales that might potentially be used to measure autistic behaviors in the general population.[33] All of these scales also incorporate some measure of social deficits. These measures suffer from the same methodological problems as discussed previously.

Adaptive Behavior Measures

Another approach to documenting the social deficits in ASD is the use of measures of social adaptive skills. Section V of Table 6.1 lists the most commonly used measures of adaptive behavior. All are available in both parent and teacher versions for comparison of behavior across settings.

Volkmar et al.[123] reported that persons with ASD typically score lower on measures of adaptive behavior than on cognitive tests. Freeman et al.[31] and more recently Kenworthy et al.[54] reported that while adaptive changes in communication skills are positively related to IQ scores, changes in social skills were not. These results confirm the use of adaptive functioning measures in assessing changes in adaptive deficits even in higher-functioning individuals with ASD. Furthermore, the relationship between social abilities and ASD exists independent of intelligence. These results also support the separate measurement of social and communication skills as communication skills are directly related to IQ.

The *Vineland Adaptive Behavior Scales, Second Edition*,[114] is probably the most widely used and researched in ASD. In addition to norms for typically developing children, this scale provides separate norms for children with ASD. It can be used to measure severity of ASD. The Vineland-II tool assesses skills in four domains: communication, daily living skills, socialization and motor skills. The scale also includes a maladaptive behavior index. Each domain is further subdivided into three subdomains. For example, the socialization domain is further divided to assess interpersonal relationships, play and leisure time, and coping skills in the home and community. The Vineland-II scale and other measures of adaptive behavior ask whether the child exhibits the skill and if that behavior occurs independently and consistently. The scales measure actual behaviors, not potential behaviors.

The *Adaptive Behavior Assessment System, Second Edition* (ABAS-II),[43] measures adaptive behavior skills from birth to 89 years. It is divided into several forms in three age groupings: 0–5 years, 5–21 years, and adult. As with the Vineland scale, separate forms are available for teachers and parents. The ABAS-II divides skills into three primary domains that cover 10 skill areas: conceptual (communication, functional pre-academic/academics, self-direction), social (leisure, social), and practical (community use, home living/school living, health and safety, self-care, work). While persons with ASD are included in the norms, separate norms for this population are not available. To date, little research has focused on the use of the ABAS-II in ASD and no specific profile for ASD has been identified.

The *Scales of Independent Behavior—Revised* (SIB-R)[17] is designed to measure adaptive behavior from infancy to mature adults. Measured skill areas include the following:

- Motor skills (gross and fine)
- Social interaction and communication skills (social interaction, language comprehension, and language expression)
- Personal living skills (eating/meal preparation, toileting, dressing, personal self-care, and domestic skills)
- Community living skills (time and punctuality, money and value, work skills, and home/community orientation)
- Maladaptive behaviors (internalized, asocial, and externalized)

As with the ABAS-II, little, if any, research into how persons with ASD score on this measure has been conducted.

In general, measures of adaptive behavior provide normative assessment data to assess social deficits in ASD. They can be utilized to identify gross strengths and weaknesses, and to measure changes over time. Unfortunately, such instruments tend to measure social skills globally and do not provide enough information to design treatment programs.

Diagnostic Measures Specific to ASD

The *Autism Diagnostic Interview—Revised* (ADI-R)[105] and the *Autism Diagnostic Observation Schedule* (ADOS)[70] are based on the *DSM-IV* criteria for autistic disorder[2, 130] and represent the gold standard for diagnosis. The ADI-R is a semi-structured interview that contains five sections: opening questions, communication, social development and play, repetitive and restricted behavior, and general behavior problems. Behaviors are rated on a 0–3 scale and are coded as to whether they occurred before or after age 5 years. The reciprocal social interaction items map directly onto the *DSM-IV*—namely, peer relationships, sharing enjoyment, and social–emotional reciprocity. Because of its length, the ADI-R is primarily used as a diagnostic research instrument.

The *Autism Diagnostic Observation Schedule* (ADOS)[70] is a highly structured behavioral observation instrument for assessment of social interactions, communication, play, and imaginative use of toys—each rated on a scale of 0–3. It consists of four modules that are administered based on the child's or adult's age and level of language development. The reciprocal social interaction items include such behaviors as use of eye contact, nonverbal communication, directing facial expressions to others, shared enjoyment in interaction, communication, affect, and understanding emotions, as well as insight into one's own behavior. The ADOS may be helpful in identifying basic social deficits in a highly structured situation, but it does not provide any information on the presence or absence of these behaviors in the natural environment.

The *Social Responsiveness Scale* (SRS)[23] is the only available instrument specifically designed as not only a diagnostic tool, but also as a measure of severity of ASD symptoms. This 65-item rating scale is completed by the primary caregiver and/or the teacher. It focuses on the child's ability to engage in emotionally appropriate reciprocal social interaction and communication. Its strength is its ability to measure severity of ASD symptoms in the natural environment. The SRS measures social awareness, social cognition, social communication, social motivation, and autistic mannerisms, and provides an overall score. The SRS has been used not only to measure severity of symptoms, but also to evaluate response to treatment.[95] This scale may be helpful in identifying which areas are most problematic for an individual child with ASD and where to focus treatment.

Assessment for Intervention

Assessment of social skills deficits is an essential part of diagnostic evaluation as well as treatment. While numerous scales are available that are designed to measure social skills, few have been standardized on children on the autism spectrum. Furthermore, while some scales have age-related norms, few have a sample of ASD persons in their normative data. Again, while social skill scales may well measure skill deficits, they do not measure social competence, thus making them of limited use in designing treatment programs.

As mentioned earlier, Reichow and Volkmar reviewed evidence-based social skills training models and concluded that some do meet criteria for evidence-based treatment.[99] In their review, these researchers used a wide variety of measures to assess outcome, ranging from standardized measures of global social behavior (e.g., Vineland, ADOS) to observational measures of specific behaviors operationalized and measured for a particular study. While both levels of measurement are important, lack of a general measure of social skills makes comparisons across studies difficult.

The only other measures specific to ASD are the *Matson Evaluation of Social Skills with Youngsters* (MESSY)[76] and the *Matson Evaluation of Social Skills for Individuals with Severe Mental Retardation* (MESSIER).[74] With these tools, 85 items are rated on a 0–3 scale and reference many of the behaviors associated with ASD, ranging from looking at the caregiver to complex skills such as giving compliments. Matson and colleagues reported that the MESSY instrument was useful in identifying target skills for intervention in students with ASD.[77] These scales are most beneficial in assessing children with more severe impairments.

One inventory that shows promise for general use in ASD is the *Social Skills Improvement System* (SSiS).[39] The SSiS is a multirater approach that includes ratings from the parent, teacher, and student. It can be used to document the frequency of perceived positive behaviors (communication, cooperation, assertion, responsibility, empathy, engagement, and self-control) along with a brief measure of problem behaviors (externalizing problems, bullying, hyperactivity/inattention, internalizing problems, and autism spectrum behaviors). National norms were used to clarify results as representative of social skills strengths, social skills performance deficits, or acquisition deficits with or without problem behaviors. These results have been linked directly to instructional lessons in the *SSiS Intervention Guide*. The SSiS represents a step in the right direction toward developing an appropriate measure of not only social skills, but also social competence in the ASD population.

Behavior Assessment

Much has been written elsewhere about behavior assessments.[45, 106, 118, 122] As with most other behavior assessments, those directed at social skills include—often at their core—objective, contemporaneous, observational measurement. That is, an individual is observed in natural (and sometimes contrived) social circumstances, and information (including presence or absence, frequency, duration, and quality) related to specific social behaviors is recorded. Behavior assessments also frequently include reports of significant parties (e.g. parents, teachers, and even peers) and document review (e.g., progress reports, individualized educational plans [IEPs], and formal testing as described earlier in this chapter). Questionnaires and scales that are designed specifically for the particular child and specifically for his or her social skill assessment, or that are published for overall (or specifically social) criteria-based behavior assessment but are not norm referenced (see, for example. the ABLLS[120] and the VB-MAPP[119]), may be used to assist in the behavior assessment process.

When a social behavior assessment is complete specific, multiple-source information is obtained through objective measurement on the behavioral functioning of an individual, in terms of both social deficits and competencies. This specific and individualized information can be readily used to inform a specific treatment or education plan as well as to measure change over time. This is a strength lacking in most of the tests reviewed earlier in this chapter. Because they do not involved standardized, norm-referenced instruments, however, the information obtained through behavior assessments cannot accurately be compared to information for typically developing peers or other children with ASD. Further, because specific individualized information is pinpointed, idiosyncratic measurement may occur (that is, only measurement of unique, small, or even minimally pertinent segments of social competency may be involved), such that overall social functioning is not sufficiently assessed.

An example of one social skills behavior assessment protocol can be found in this book. A segment of Chapter 7 walks the reader through the behavior assessment process and highlights the use of the social skills taxonomy (Chapter 8) to guide and assist not only the assessment of skill deficits and competencies, but also the development of necessary instructional programming.

Summary

The field of social skills assessment for individuals with ASD is somewhat narrow but growing. New tools are being developed that are designed for a variety of purposes and that focus on various aspects of the social skills arena. While some instruments have particular strengths, no one test provides the breadth of information that may be necessary to sufficiently treat and educate a person with ASD in the social realm. As with most assessments, the use of multiple sources and multiple modes, including individualized behavior assessments, will generate the most comprehensive and interventionally functional representation of the social weakness and strengths of an individual with ASD.

7

Creating Curricula: Task and Strategic Analysis

Karen McKinnon

Teaching social skills can seem an overwhelming task. Initially, you must decide which specific social skills are important for a child to learn and whether a child is ready to learn that particular skill. Once you know the social skills you are aiming for, it is a complex process to break down elusive social concepts, such as "apologizing" or "interrupting" or "compromising," into tangible programs that a child can be taught.

Given the complex and ever-changing nature of social beings, social skills are required to be dynamic and fluid. There are subtle differences in the way we interact depending on who we are interacting with. We need to have a broad array of social competencies to meet the range of social circumstances that life brings. Given these facts, it is impossible to have a comprehensive curriculum that lists all possible social skills a child needs to learn. We can't just tick off social skills on a list, because these skills need to be applied in a range of social contexts, within different families, peer groups, communities, and cultures.

In many cases, we know that some explicit social rules must be imparted to our children: Don't hit other children, look when you are speaking to your teacher, answer someone when they talk to you, and so on. At other times, the nuances of social interaction seem less clear. How is it that we know when to give a compliment and when to hold off? Sometimes, there may be a social rule at play, but the rule may be difficult to define. At other times, great discretion may be necessary.

Given the range of social behaviors that are necessary for most individuals to succeed in their interpersonal world, and given the range of social needs often exhibited by children with autism spectrum disorder (ASD),[75, 126] it is impossible to create an exhaustive curriculum of social skills for this population. The skills presented in the Curriculum section of this book are intended to provide instructional content for social skills training on a number of specific needs common to individuals with ASD. At the same time, the social skills provided are intended to serve another purpose—to serve as examples of specific social programs under a social skills taxonomy classification system (see Chapter 8). In this way, as specific needs arise for a particular child, additional individualized curricula can be developed for that child based on those models. The process of creating new and specific social skills curricula under the taxonomy is the focus of this chapter. As parents, educators, or other professionals, we can work through a number of steps to determine and develop the social skills a child needs to learn. We can go through a process that expertly breaks these skills down into tangible programs, while ensuring that eventually the child with ASD can put it all together in a way that is functional and meaningful within society.

The Process of Curriculum Development

The development of social goals and tasks can be divided into four steps. Initially, we assess the social skills of the individual child to develop an inventory of that child's unique profile of skills and deficits. From this information, we examine the child's profile and create a list of broad social goals that the child will need to learn at some point in the future. Then, we determine the priority social goals that the child should be taught now. Finally, we break these social goals down into units of information that the child can learn and then gradually establish the child's independent and full competency in the ability—all the while ensuring that we preserve the essence and intent of the skill, along with the final goal of the child independently using the skill in his or her natural social world.

Step 1: Assessment of Social Skills and Deficits

We can gather information about the child's current social skills and behaviors. What are this child's established social skills? What are this child's social deficits? If we can answer these questions, the information will point us in the direction of possible goals to teach the child.

A functional behavior assessment[92] may be useful to capture the nature of a child's social deficits. Inappropriate social behaviors serve a function (e.g., attention seeking, escape from a social situation, control of others in play). If we can understand the function of a child's social behaviors, we can come up with meaningful ways of addressing these behaviors. For example, if a child is displaying behavior that is "over the top" in an attempt to get a peer's attention (e.g., falling over and laughing, making silly faces, getting up close to the peer's face and making strange sounds), we can teach him or her to seek attention in other ways (e.g., pursuing a peer to share an exciting item or activity; commenting on or complimenting something the peer is doing). Often, we need to understand the reason behind the behavior so that we can identify a skill deficit and come up with a practical and meaningful replacement skill that the child can be taught.

Information about the child can also come from formal assessments (e.g., psychological testing, speech pathology evaluations). These information-gathering efforts may provide some insight into a child's social competence in a formal manner and, when testing is norm-based, in comparison to the child's peers. Additionally, social skills checklists or assessment tools may assist us in capturing a child's current social functioning, while also allowing us to track progress over time. Chapter 6 provides more information on testing and assessment in this area.

Formal (scheduled, structured, and/or written) and informal behavior assessment can be very helpful in identifying social needs (see Chapter 6). This type of evaluation can include obtaining reports from several sources. For example, family members, teachers, and childcare staff can provide background and general information about the child's social behavior across a variety of circumstances and settings. Obtaining information from multiple sources can be facilitative. For example, even when reports indicate that a child can play with siblings at home, he or she may not reliably engage with peers in other social settings. Gathering information from a variety of sources assists the process of identifying needs: If we know what a child is like in a variety of situations, we will know the range of social skills we need to target.

Behavior assessments also involve direct (not just reported) observation of the child in social situations. Such observations can provide invaluable information on actual social functioning in the social situation. (Watching peers, unfortunately, often makes clear the depth of the child's own social deficits.) It is recommended that multiple observations are conducted—so patterns of responding can be identified—in a variety of settings and under a range of circumstances, to obtain a broad sense of social competencies and deficits. These observations may include times when the child is interacting with familiar family members at home (e.g., playing with a cousin on the trampoline, chatting while eating a snack with Grandma); interacting with peers at the local playground, a birthday party, or at school, in structured (e.g., during a basketball game) or unstructured (e.g., at the beach) social contexts; with small or large groups of peers; and with familiar and unfamiliar children.

When assessing a child, it can be helpful to create a list of social skills. This list will be useful to examine in later stages of the curriculum development process. It allows you to bring together all the information you have collected from a range of sources. An example for Madison, aged four, is provided in the following table. Madison was observed at kindergarten during outdoor free play, during indoor free play, and within a structured matching game with a teacher and one peer. Her parents also reported on her social interaction with other family members.

As social strengths and weaknesses are being examined, the assessor can use the social skills taxonomy (see Chapter 8) to bring order and focus to the process of establishing a sense of social needs. For example, looking at the area of *social awareness*, one can potentially discern the following skills: Is the child even noticing others? Can he or she follow the play theme? Is he or she picking up on the nonverbal cues of other people? Does he or she have enough knowledge of popular culture (e.g., music, TV, movies, computer and console games)? Does the child have a sense of another's perspective? Does he or she display any behaviors that other children might think odd? Thinking of *social communication*, one can consider the following issues: Can the child follow and engage in the conversational topic, interrupt appropriately, apologize at the right times, and communicate gauging appropriate personal space? Considering *social interaction*, the assessor can examine the following skills: Is the child responding to the initiations of others and initiating interactions him or herself? Does the child change behaviors based on other's reactions? Is he or she capable of assertion, negotiation, or problem solving? Within the category of *social learning*, a parent or professional can consider these questions: Is the child readily learning from

MADISON'S PROFILE OF SOCIAL SKILLS AND DEFICITS

ESTABLISHED SKILLS	EMERGING SKILLS (THESE NEED SOME CONSOLIDATION)	DEFICITS
Initiates comments to peers	Responds to peer comments (sometimes responds, sometimes ignores)	Wants to control the play, have it go her way
Thinks of creative ideas for play (good imagination)	Eye contact (occurs usually when she is talking, not when she is meant to be listening to others)	Dismisses peer ideas in play
Topical knowledge (has plenty of relevant things to talk about with peers)	Responding to adults (responds to familiar adults, but not unfamiliar teachers)	Gets angry when she cannot be the main character
Responds to most adult questions		Struggles to wait for her turn to speak/ taking turns
Responds positively to social attention		Interrupts teachers and peers when they are speaking
Is very motivated to be with peers		Tries to dominate peers—selects a friend for the day and rejects any other social advances by other peers

the social actions of peers? Does the child stay with the group when they move on? Does the peer culture seem to readily "rub off" on the child? Finally, employing the notion of *social relatedness,* the assessor can examine these issues: Is the child socially interested? Does he or she have joint attention? Does the child show genuine empathy?

Using the taxonomy may, by directing your attention to specific areas, help you notice nuanced and subtle areas of need, as well as gross deficits. Further, it may assist in arranging, organizing, and managing (and ultimately prioritizing) what might otherwise seem an overwhelming volume of targets and goals.

Step 2: Defining Broad Goals

In the example of Madison, there seems to be a common theme within the deficit areas. She wants to control what others do and say. She interrupts others to dominate with her own ideas. Socially, it seems that Madison is too focused on her own desires and needs. She does not show adequate skills in allowing other people to have their say, share their thoughts or comments, or take their turn in social games. She demonstrates consistent difficulty in the social interaction area. We could consider the social deficit underlying all of these examples to be a lack of "social interactional reciprocity." In kid-friendly language, perhaps we can call it "sometimes letting other people be the leader."

Regarding the deficits Madison may show in social relatedness (such as in empathy and consideration), it may be valid to teach Madison to understand how other people feel when she doesn't let them have a turn and to show caring in response. Although we may teach her to share interactional control, she may demonstrate this behavior only because we have told her to do so.

Conversely, we cannot assume that knowledge and growth in empathy and consideration will serve as a sufficient incentive for Madison to change how she behaves. Although she may care about the other person's right to speak (after developing such capacities), she may still care about being in control herself to a much greater extent! We may still need to work on the interactional reciprocity issue. Thus we have come up with two broad goals for Madison: She needs to learn to let other people occasionally be in control and we want her to understand and care about the perspective of others.

When, using the taxonomy for assistance, you can organize the list of social deficits into a few key areas, as we have done for Madison, doing so enables you to have a global sense of the most important areas to focus upon. Common themes may come through, such as "reading subtle cues," "staying on topic," "maintaining the flow of conversation," "initiating," "responding," "letting others do it their way," "learning from others," or "socially referencing." Themes such as these, along with the taxonomy framework, can help you develop a broad, overall picture of the child's social needs and goals. You can also begin to develop a sense of ranking of specific deficits within these broad areas—identifying which skills may be more requisite, beginning, or foundational than others. Of course, some children may demonstrate much scattering in their social deficits, in which case consolidation into thematic areas may be difficult. Even in such cases, however, some collapsing of specific deficiencies into areas of need may be possible. Utilization of the taxonomy in such situations may also help in classifying needs and setting up progressions of targets from basic to intermediate to more advanced.

Step 3: Deciding What to Teach Right Now

From this list of broad social goals, how do we decide what is a priority to work on right now? A number of variables must be considered when answering that question. Think of a child you know, and a particular social skill you would like that child to learn. With that example in mind, answer the following questions by placing a mark in the appropriate box:

If I teach this social skill, will it result in better peer relationships, greater general success in the child's peer culture, and reduced social stigma for the child?

☐ No impact on general success and peer relationships

☐ Some limited impact on success and peer relationships

☐ Some positive impact on success and peer relationships

☐ Significantly improved peer culture success and peer relationships

If I teach this social skill, will it result in a better quality of life for the child in his or her family and social world?

> ☐ No impact on quality of life
>
> ☐ Some limited impact on quality of life
>
> ☐ Some positive impact quality of life
>
> ☐ Significantly improved quality of life

Will this skill be a building block for more advanced social skills in future (e.g., a child needs to be responsive to the social initiations of others so that sustained interactions can be developed in the future)?

> ☐ Not pivotal to or requisite for other skills; an isolated skill
>
> ☐ Teaching this skill may affect one other area
>
> ☐ Teaching this skill will provide a basis for at least two other social skills, or will serve as a prerequisite for other social areas
>
> ☐ This social skill is a building block for a whole range of social skills in future

If your responses fall toward the latter responses in each area, you should consider the social skill to be an important area of learning for the child, and it should be prioritized accordingly. We aim to teach social skills that are functional for a child to use both now and in the future. Isolated skills may not be such a priority. For example, it's probably more important for the child with ASD to initiate interactions with friends when they are available, so they can chat and play throughout the day, rather than to spend a lot of time learning to say "please" when he or she asks for something at home. Initiating with peers is critical to social relationships in every setting; saying "please" is not. More time should be focused on the areas of highest social impact. As another example, it may be nominally useful to teach a child to take turns during a social game. Truly enriching social experiences (and facilitations of social interest) will result when a child is taught to interact, engage in banter, and actually compete to win during social play.

A number of other considerations must be taken into account when deciding what to teach. Information about typical developmental milestones guides us in understanding which skills are achievable and typical for children of a certain age. Look at the social skills of other peers who are the same age as the child with ASD. Spend time observing a range of different children. You will notice a cluster of social skills that almost all children at the same age can perform—these are the skills you want the child with ASD to learn. If, in a specific setting, community, or culture, a particular social skill is not common in other children, then it's not very important for the child with ASD either. For example, parents often like their child to learn to say "Excuse me?" if he or she has not heard what an adult has said. When you observe most children around 15 years of age, the more natural response is actually "What?" or "Huh?" As adults, we may not like it, but if we want the child with ASD to blend in with other children, we may just have to be satisfied with hearing "Huh?"

When a large gap exists between the social abilities of the child with ASD and those of his or her peer group, placing importance on developmental norms may be less crucial. For children who are still in the early stages of social skill development, the curriculum may focus on building solid foundation skills such as orienting to people, building tolerance to social settings or situations (e.g., becoming comfortable in large groups, or tolerating sharing the attention of a parent with a neighbor who has called in for coffee), imitating peer play or actions, responding to the initiation of others, developing some degree of social interest and desire, and showing self-control over stigmatizing behaviors.

Consider also whether a child has all the necessary skills to perform a social skill. "Conversation" is a social skill we sometimes promote too early in a child's social development. When you break down all the components of a conversation (e.g., maintaining eye contact, reading nonverbal body language, comprehension, making statements, answering questions, staying on a relevant topic, having the general knowledge about a subject area to have something to say, truly desiring to engage in reciprocal communication with another), it's easy to see why conversation falls apart for some children when we try to teach it. It's only when a child has mastered all of these requisite skills that he or she can (and would desire to) hold a meaningful and authentic conversation without needing any prompting or support.

Step 4: Task and Strategic Analysis

Once you have determined the broad areas the child needs to work on and decided on the high-priority social goals, these tasks need to be broken down into teachable (or, perhaps more importantly, learnable) components. This process is commonly called task analysis.[118] Further, creating and ordering segments (phases) of learning that will allow for the successful acquisition of the skill will need to occur (such as in the curriculum of *A Work in Progress*[65]). This process is referred to as strategic analysis.

Social skills are often incredibly complex, nuanced, and sophisticated. It can be difficult to work out exactly how to take the essence of a social skill and turn it into a teachable program. How do we teach joint attention so that a child not only looks at another but truly socially references and desires to share orientation? How do we teach a child not only the steps to initiate an

77

interaction with another, but the social interest and desire to actively pursue a social interchange? How do we teach a child to make empathic statements, while simultaneously instilling a true emotional connection to another's experience?

Consider what might seem to be the straightforward act of "interrupting" others. In addition to teaching the responses of interrupting, style and manner components must be addressed. Then there is the issue of knowing when it's appropriate to interrupt another person. There are numerous cues to read, and timing considerations in response to those cues. Further, an unwritten social etiquette seems to govern the times when it's acceptable to interrupt someone and the times when it's not. The decision can change depending on who is speaking: For example, it might be okay for a child to interrupt his peers when conversing at snack time, but it is not okay to interrupt a teacher when she is speaking to the class. But, then again, it is okay to interrupt the teacher if it's an emergency! Clearly, there are complicated rules at play here. Having a full sense of all facets of a skill, including those elements that may differentiate the rote from the authentic, is critical to breaking that skill down, building it up, and ultimately instilling it in another.

We use a number of methods to understand and break down social skills. Some of these guidelines apply to the task and strategic analysis of any skill or behavior, not just social skills. However, social skills warrant a great deal of thought due to their complex and often elusive nature.

How to Conduct a Task and Strategic Analysis

- Perform the skill yourself.
  Enter into a social situation where the skill you will be teaching is required. Think about the steps you are performing. Examine the context and consider how your behavior differs from one situation to another. An example is "giving compliments." When do you give a compliment to someone else? When do you refrain? Do you change your compliment depending on the target audience or the setting? How do you know when is a good time to give a compliment?
- Watch a competent and relevant peer perform the skill.
  Many times we—as adults—interact differently as compared to children of a given age. Rather than relying on an adult model of interaction, observe a peer (or a number of peers) perform the skill. Notice how this skill is performed in the relevant and immediate peer setting and culture. Examine the way a peer uses the social skill. It might also be beneficial to watch a peer with deficits, as that exercise may help clarify which deficits are critical.
- Use an established task analysis as a base.
  The process of task analysis is incredibly individualized. Established curricula, such as those provided in this book, can provide a great starting point for understanding how to break social skills down into teachable components. You can use this information as a basis for further investigation and analysis. As you read through established programs, you will have to assess which phases are relevant for the specific child and which phases you can skip. There will also be gaps in the program that you will need to fill in yourself, so as to put your own unique spin on the social skill for the child.

- Include all the relevant components.

  What is done, what is said, how it is said, nonverbal aspects, supportive aspects (e.g., calming breath before speaking), internal components (e.g., decision trees, self-talk), and elements that pertain to intent, desire, and emotion (i.e., that capture authenticity and essence of the skill)—all are critical in enabling a child to truly master a social skill. It is recommended that, to avoid rote responding when possible, variations of elements (e.g., different ways to say the same thing) are identified.

- Determine what would constitute learnable segments for the particular individual.

  It is common practice to segment a task based on what seem to be natural break points in the action or endeavor. In reality, it may be much more helpful to generate components that are of a size and form most easily learned by the student. For example, some children need to spend time learning a number of different sentence stems when commenting in play, whereas other children can skip this phase because they already display natural variation in language.

- Arrange the teaching of the task in an order that will facilitate its ultimate acquisition.

  This aspect of planning usually means determining which parts are prerequisite to others. It can also involve recognizing that establishing other or related skills first may be necessary to successfully address the specific task at hand (e.g., teaching "cause and effect" will be necessary for students to learn to become aware of the effect of their behavior on others). In addition, it may mean first addressing components that result in easy, initial success, in order to promote student effort as later, more challenging skill elements are addressed. If teaching proceeds in an optimal order, it may also engender some savings in the learning process (e.g., quicker acquisition when the more challenging components are introduced).

- Include as necessary tactics to assist in the acquisition of the competency.

  This part of the learning experience may include chaining, shaping, prompting and prompt fading, and priming. It may also include suggestions for the additional breaking down of skills—even further than initially planned—when a student is struggling with acquisition. Generalization plans, which are necessary for transitioning learning to application of skills in everyday social situations, are a must. Strategies that are most likely to facilitate independent acquisition and performance should be emphasized.

- Attempt to not just identify responses, but also distill intent, emotional content, and the "essence" of authentic social skills in guiding what and how skills are taught.

  Preserving these elements can mean the difference in establishing authentic skills as opposed to merely teaching rote or mechanical performance. See the curriculum sections on empathy and social interest for examples of how this can be done.

- Consult a professional.

  If you need additional assistance, it can be helpful to rely on a practitioner who has experience in task and strategic analysis of social skills. This person can assist you to gather information, break the skill down, and determine exactly how to teach it to a specific child.

Remembering the End Goal: A Problematic Example

Obviously, the goal of teaching a social skill is that the child appropriately uses the skill he or she has been taught! The task and strategic analysis needs to reflect this desired end. Consider the following flawed task analysis, relating to teaching a child to initiate greeting others:

Step 1: A person walks into the room.

Step 2: The child looks at the person.

Step 3: The child says, "Hi."

Step 4: If the child does not say hello, therapist should say, "What do you say?"; the child should then say, "Hi."

If a therapist uses this task analysis, it will result in the child saying hello to every person who enters the room! The child has not learned to discriminate when it is appropriate to say hello and when it is not. For example, we typically say hello if it is the first time we have seen someone in that day, but we don't say hello again after that. Or, we may say hello the first time we see the person; if the individual then leaves the house for an outing and returns later, we may greet the person again. We may call out "Hi" if the setting is at home with family, but we usually don't call out "Hi" if we're sitting in assembly at school. Clearly, greeting others is a lot more complicated than just enforcing a rule of saying hello when someone enters a room.

The second step of the preceding analysis states that the child looks at the person. But does the child truly desire to do this? Has he or she been taught to orient to a person merely when an individual enters a room? Does he or she truly want to know or see who it is or what that person may be doing? Would the child want to see who it is when he or she is engaged in only boring tasks or even when he or she is engrossed in extremely stimulating activities? If the requisite skill of orienting to a person because of social interest, curiosity, or desire has not been addressed, then the child will not likely learn to independently greet people in a socially authentic way.

Additionally, this flawed task analysis creates a dependence on a third person to facilitate the greeting. The child may completely miss the fact that someone has walked into the room and may merely be responding to the therapist prompt "What do you say?" by answering "Hi" by rote. A good strategic analysis will preempt situations where dependence may occur and will plan for teaching a skill to complete independence.

To further complicate the situation, sometimes it will be the child who is walking into the room, not the other person. The child then has to discriminate whether to say hello in this situation. Every different angle of greetings should be explored. This does not mean that you need to teach every possible scenario. Rather, you need to teach a sufficient number of examples until the child picks up on the concept or generalized ability. The overall goal of teaching a greeting is that the child becomes aware of the context and uses a greeting if the situation is befitting of it (and again, while retaining a social purpose for doing so). The task and strategic analysis needs to reflect all of these variations in context and, ultimately, the skill needs to transfer to novel settings and situations.

It can be helpful to teach the black-and-white situations first, then try to fill in the grayer situations later on, once a child has a basic understanding of the social rules. Using this framework, think about the ways a child can handle social conflict, such as peer saying that a child cannot join in a game. It's never acceptable for a child to use physical aggression to solve this problem. It's always a good idea for the child to try to negotiate his or her inclusion in the group using words. The gray area is when a child should stand his or her ground and keep negotiating to join the group versus when he or she should walk away. Similarly, it might be appropriate try to negotiate with Dad for extra time on the computer at home, but it's not likely to be acceptable to negotiate with the school principal about the time school should end every day!

Conversely, sometimes it may not be wise to teach some skills in a rote or scripted manner initially, if the goal is authentic skill establishment. It may be better to teach a smaller part of the skill (e.g., simply orienting to a person when the individual walks in), while preserving its essential quality as much as possible, rather than requiring a child to merely perform the whole skill set in a rote fashion.

It takes a deep understanding of the objectives of teaching a particular social skill to break it down in a useful and practical way. Keep in mind the end goal—use of an authentic skill in the natural setting.

Putting It All Together: A Positive Example

To complete this chapter, an example of the process of curriculum development is provided. The example concerns a child, Sam, and an area of social need. Sam's therapeutic team has completed Steps 1 through 3 of the curriculum development process and has decided that, under the taxonomy areas of social communication and interaction, Sam needs to learn the social skill of "interrupting." Provided here is the task and strategic analysis (Step 4) created to teach Sam how to appropriately interrupt others in his daily life. Commentary on the development of these steps is provided to guide the reader along the process. The completed instructional content for interrupting is also included in the Curriculum section of this book.

First, some background on Sam:

> Sam is eight years old and has very sound verbal skills. He attends a mainstream school where an assistant supports him in the classroom and playground. He often interrupts the teacher when she is speaking to the whole class (because he has something he feels is very important to share). He interrupts his parents when they are speaking to each other, and when his mother is on the phone. Sam was also

observed to frequently interrupt his peers when it is their turn to share information with the class. Some of these peers are becoming frustrated with Sam for constantly interrupting them. At play times, Sam will interrupt the people he plays with when they are explaining rules of games, or generally chatting. Most often, Sam interrupts because he believes what he has to say is very important to share. It is usually information about himself and his own interests or desires.

Commentary

After initially identifying the specific goal, Sam's team specified the main objectives of teaching Sam how to interrupt. These are the goals his parents and teachers defined for Sam, given what they observed of him at school and at home. As you can see, these objectives will guide the content of the task analysis. By developing the objectives of the program, the team gets a very clear picture of exactly which skills Sam needs to learn.

Program Title: Interrupting Others

Objectives

1. To help Sam recognize when someone is busy in interaction and conversation (and, therefore, to help him understand that he will be interrupting if he speaks at that time)
2. To teach Sam to evaluate indicators of appropriate times to interrupt others
3. To help Sam recognize circumstances under which interrupting is more or less appropriate
4. To help Sam discriminate whether his information is really important and, therefore, worthy of an interruption
5. To teach Sam to demonstrate a range of appropriate methods of interrupting, and apply these techniques to different situations and audiences as the situation requires
6. To teach Sam to accept a delay before he can interrupt others, and to occupy himself appropriately during this delay
7. To teach Sam to refrain from interrupting when offers are refused or when it has been occurring with too great a frequency

Commentary

Once the objectives have been determined, the team develops a conceptual understanding of the skill of interrupting. Sam's team members reflect on how they all perform the skill of interrupting in their own lives. They think about all the situations in which interrupting may occur and all the considerations that come into play. They reflect on the tools and skills that are necessary to successfully interrupt and interact under such circumstances. When Sam's therapy team members share their findings, they come away with some valuable information. This is collated with the information they have gathered from watching how other children who are Sam's age interrupt in a variety of settings and situations. A list of observations and considerations, and possible teaching phases, is generated from these findings:

- People seem to interrupt in a number of ways:
  - If a person is talking, you can talk over the top of that individual (e.g., ask a question, make a comment).
  - If a person is talking, you can try to "catch the individual's eye," wait to see if he or she acknowledges you, and then wait until the person finishes his or her conversation and turns to you. If you are waiting, you still need to "check in" with that person to see that he or she remembers you are waiting.
  - If a person is talking, you can wait for a pause in the conversation, and then add your own comment or question.
  - If the person is busy at a task (but not talking to someone), you can say, "Excuse me?" and wait for the person to look up. You might possibly repeat this behavior a number of times.
  - If a group of people are talking or busy at a task, all the same guidelines still apply.

- People almost always interrupt if it's an emergency (but we would need to ensure Sam understands what "emergency" means).
- Different people interrupt with different levels of assertiveness. Some people are quite passive, and tend to wait for pauses in the conversation or activity. Others are very dominant, and tend to err on the side of talking over the top of the person. The activity of the other person influences one's level of assertiveness.
- When you interrupt someone, you need to read his or her reaction to see if the person values the interruption, or if it bothers the person. If it bothers the person, don't interrupt again
- Children at Sam's age are able to identify natural opportunities to interrupt (e.g., a pause in conversation, an adult looking up from a task and making eye contact). Thus this recognition is a developmentally appropriate skill for Sam to learn
- Children tend to interrupt each other during play by talking over the top of each other, whereas adults expect children to wait until the adults are finished what they are doing or saying before speaking.
- When children interrupt, they employ a number of other skills at the same time. These include maintaining appropriate personal space, reading nonverbal body language, tolerating waiting, providing on-topic conversation, and demonstrating assertiveness (being brave enough to interrupt someone in a social setting). These are all prerequisites to good interrupting abilities
- Sam knows *why* he wants to interrupt (to share his ideas), but not *if, when,* or *how* to interrupt.

Given these considerations, the team can detail the prerequisite skills Sam needs to have in place before he can embark on the skill of interrupting. The observations and considerations will also guide decision making on the phase of the curriculum as well as the skills' order and strategy of introduction.

Prerequisites

- Frustration tolerance, impulse control, and waiting
- Assertiveness
- Environmental awareness (awareness of the presence of others)
- Basic social initiation
- Reading basic nonverbal social cues
- Waiting
- Intermediate conversation and interactional skills

Commentary

The team members now have a clear picture of exactly what they want to teach Sam (the objectives), the prerequisite skills he needs to have in place prior to commencing this program, and all the considerations relating to the skill of interrupting. These elements must now be translated into learnable program phases, which will allow Sam to master some of the most essential aspects of interrupting, then ensure that the skill can be generalized.

Initially, the team needs to examine which areas may necessarily precede others (e.g., be prerequisite to or facilitative of later learning) and determine how to structure the instruction to promote acquisition. It is decided that Sam first needs to be able to identify several social cues (e.g., timing of interruption, urgency indicators) for the rest of the interrupting skills to be performed. It is also determined that discrimination training (see *A Work in Progress*) will be utilized to promote such learning.

PHASE 1: Why Important and When to Use (Recognizing When Someone Is Busy). The focus of this phase is to provide the *why* and the *when* of interrupting. The child is given rationales for appropriate interrupting skills and choices. Further effort is directed toward teaching the child to identify when someone is busy versus available. This discrimination will aid the child in evaluating exactly when interrupting skills need to be applied (i.e., if the individual is not occupied, then interrupting would not occur, and mere social initiation skills would be utilized).

Reasons for Interrupting in an Appropriate Manner

The child is provided rationales for utilizing appropriate interruption skills and strategies as well as for the problematic results of inappropriate interrupting.

Rationales might include the following:

- You are more likely to get what you want if you interrupt your parents in a way that doesn't upset or annoy them.
- Appropriate interruption might actually get people to listen better and more quickly to you (because they stop and lecture you for bothering them when you interrupt in a poor way).
- People will listen when it's really important (because you won't have "cried wolf").
- People will stop ignoring you.
- You might get to join in more often.

When to Use Interrupting: Are People Busy?

The child will learn when to use his or her interrupting tools, by discriminating if others are actually preoccupied in a task or conversation. The child should be able to discriminate if someone is busy within situations like the following:

- Two adults are talking
- Two adults are in proximity but not currently interacting
- A teacher is talking to the class
- The teacher is promoting unstructured discussion
- The teacher is talking to another or small group of students
- Two or more peers are talking to each other

- Two or more peers are not talking to each other but are concentrating on what they are doing
- Two or more peers are engaged in an unstructured conversational "free for all"
- An adult or child is engaged in a preoccupying activity (without other people interacting)

Create two conditions: "busy" and "not busy." Have the child watch other people interacting, or engaged in solitary activities (either in role-play, on video, or in natural settings) that represent the two conditions. At different moments during the observation, the child identifies whether an identified person is busy. The child should also explain how he or she knows the person is busy/not busy, so a bank of knowledge and generalized knowledge about the way people look when they are busy and what constitutes "business" is developed. This discrimination training would look something like this:

Example 1: Busy

TEACHER: "What do you think about that person now, Sam?"

STUDENT: "He looks busy."

TEACHER: "How do you know he's busy?"

STUDENT: "Because he's talking and looking at that other boy."

Example 2: Not Busy

TEACHER: "Do you think he's busy or not busy now?"

STUDENT: "I think he's not busy."

TEACHER: "How do you know?"

STUDENT: "Because he's quiet and not really doing anything."

PHASE 2: Recognizing Timing Indicators. As in Phase 1, the child is taught through discrimination training to identify cues that indicate that, when a person is busy, interrupting could be initiated. Cues include the following:

- A pause in or the end of an activity
- A pause in conversation
- An invitation to interrupt offered by the individual
- Eye contact and positive facial expression or nonverbal positive acknowledgments offered by the individual

PHASE 3: Appropriateness Indicators. As in the preceding phases, the child is taught through discrimination training to identify situations and cues that indicate interrupting statements or questions, in this situation, are more or less appropriate. Indicators taught could include the following:

- The child has information regarding an emergency to share. Specific examples of emergencies should be taught (e.g., the need to give aid to another), but rules of what constitutes emergencies should also be taught (e.g., if action isn't taken right away, someone could be hurt).
- The other person is doing an activity that should not be interrupted. Again, specific examples should be taught, but types of activities should also be provided if possible (e.g., emergencies, activities that require full and careful attention or delicate action).
- The other has stated not to interrupt.
- The other is an adult in authority.
- Prior nonverbal cues to not interrupt have been offered (specific nonverbal cues will likely need to be taught).
- Individuals who are talking have gone to a secluded area.
- Class rules have forbidden interrupting in specific situation.
- The child has off-topic or obsessive-theme-oriented information to share.
- The child has an accomplishment to share.
- A window of opportunity for action exists for the child.
- The child wants to socially join in a conversation, activity, or interaction with peers.

If capable, the child will need to learn to weigh indicators when more than one is present, to determine the relative appropriateness of interrupting.

Commentary

Once requisite discrimination training has occurred, the team decides it is appropriate to teach some interrupting-related skills that would be required for the success of later skills. Once these related abilities are acquired, the interrupting skills themselves can be addressed

PHASE 4: Requisite Interrupting-Related Skills. These requisites should be instructed utilizing Teaching Interactions in simulations that gradually become increasingly challenging and realistic.

- Pausing before interrupting.

The child may need to learn to pause (and perhaps use self-talk or a mini relaxation moment such as taking a breath) before interrupting. This will be especially useful when the situation needs to be assessed by the child and skill element decisions need to be made. This requisite becomes especially important when matters of urgency for the child are involved and programming should gradually work toward increasing such challenges.

- Knowing waiting is required.

The child may need to be taught, through discrimination training, when an approach has been accepted, denied, or just delayed (and waiting is required). Such recognition should be taught in response to verbalizations as well as gestural cues (e.g., someone waving a palm up and down to indicate "wait" or putting the index finger up as a sign to indicate that the child has been noticed but needs to "wait a minute").

- Waiting when interrupting is delayed.

The child must often learn to tolerate a delay. Again, this skill becomes especially important when urgency is involved. The child must also learn how to occupy such wait time, without resorting to self-stimulatory or odd responding (while remembering and retaining the motivation for and the content of the interruption).

- Refraining from finishing interruption.

On some occasions, the child may begin to interrupt, but then be interrupted himself or herself. The child must tolerate not being able to finish as well as be able to desist talking and interacting until allowed to continue. Again, practice should be progressive and involve considerations, such as how long the child has been talking, how enthusiastic he or she is about the subject, and how important conveying the information is.

- Tolerating a denial.

The child must learn to handle when an attempt to interrupt is refused. Again, work should progress toward the inclusion of situations that involve matters of importance to the child.

- When and how to gain assistance.

Through discrimination training and role-play, the child should learn situations that suggest assistance is necessary (e.g., when interruptions are ignored or denied) and who to ask (e.g., a teacher, an available adult, a close peer) for help or guidance when interrupting efforts are not successful.

Commentary

Once requisite skill training has occurred, the team decides it is appropriate to teach actual skills of interrupting communication and interaction. Information from the observations and analyses of this task are incorporated into the instructional content. Interrupting skills are broken into learnable segments, which are then taught in systematic and sequential fashion. Rather than just teaching a series of mere actions, the skill instruction focuses on establishing skills that will help Sam genuinely achieve what he desires (as emphasized in the previously discussed rationales) in a socially adaptive and successful manner.

PHASE 5: Interrupting Skill Elements. In this phase, the child learns a number of skill elements that can be used to interrupt other people. Using a Teaching Interactions approach (see Chapter 2) the child will practice using these skills in a structured setting, to ensure success and fluent performance. Set up situations that require interrupting (e.g., two or more people are conversing or an individual is occupied with an engrossing activity). Incorporation of indicators learned in earlier phases will be necessary and additional finer social cue discriminations may be required. Once the child has mastered one skill element, teach the others in a similar fashion.

- Waiting for a pause or end.

The child should approach the person he or she wants to speak to, stand at an appropriate distance, wait until there is a pause in or completion of the conversation or activity, and then start speaking.

- Hand raising in class to interrupt.

The child is taught to interrupt instructional staff during small- and large-group teaching arrangements. Noticing pauses in instruction or identification of topic transition points could be incorporated, for some students, into instruction of this element.

- Talking over the top.

This skill should be used only with appropriate other parties, such as siblings and known peers. It should be taught that such an approach makes sense with joining-in interrupting or when emergencies or urgent matters need to be shared.

The child should approach the children he or she wants to speak to, stand at an appropriate distance, listen to the conversation and make sure he or she has something relevant or important to say, and then speak in a clear, loud (yet polite) voice while the others are still speaking.

- Making an interrupting statement.

The child can be taught that this method is appropriate when someone is engaged in activities or conversations, when topics other than those being discussed are to be shared, and when joining in is not the intent.

The child should wait for a pause in the conversation, and then make an interrupting statement in a polite voice, such as "Excuse me," "Hey, guys?," "I have something I really need to ask," or "Sorry to interrupt." The child will need to correctly determine whether the other person has heard the statement. The child must then assess whether the person has offered affirmative acknowledgment (e.g., says, "Yes, Sam?" or offers eye contact and an inquiring expression, or conversely says, "Just a minute, Sam"). If affirmative acknowledgment is provided, the child should then proceed with interruption. If affirmative acknowledgment is not provided, the child must learn to wait and try again. If indicators are provided that interrupting is not appropriate, the child will need to end the interruption attempt and leave.

- Proximity, eye contact, and waiting.

This method would most likely be used with adults when interruption is important but activities or conversations at hand are also relatively engrossing, preoccupying, or important. These would also be situations that are unlikely to contain frequent pauses and for which interrupting statements would not be indicated.

The child is taught to approach the person he or she wishes to interrupt and stand for a brief period (not longer than 30 seconds) at a comfortable proximity. During that time, the child orients toward the other person, attempting to make eye contact. A facial expression containing inquiring, permission requesting, and hopeful elements can be taught to the child to be utilized should eye contact be provided by the other person. If positive acknowledgment is provided, then the child can proceed with the interruption. The child is taught to leave within 30 seconds if no eye contact is given (as well as in response to direct verbal and nonverbal refusals to be interrupted).

Commentary

Once components of a skill have begun to be taught, teams may review the phases and discover that additional elements need to be added. Once a sufficient array of skills or skill elements are taught, it is typical with complex skills that the child may need to learn which elements to use when and under which circumstances. Sam's team at this point focuses on teaching him to make decisions about which skill elements to use when interrupting is indicated.

PHASE 6: Evaluating and Choosing the Best Skill to Use. Once the child has learned the range of interrupting skill elements, he or she still needs to evaluate when and how to use these skills in everyday life. This process includes deciding which skill to try first, and changing the skills utilized depending on the setting and people involved.

- Deciding which skill to use first.

This step involves the child making decisions, based on the variables and indicators listed previously as well as unfolding circumstances in the interaction, about which skill element to use. It is analogous to "Wh- discriminations" (see the Comprehension program in *A Work in Progress*) in which separate components are first taught (e.g., who, what, where) and then a program is utilized to teach the child to make discriminations (and choices) about which one applies.

The program should start by using contrived scenarios (video, role-play, or naturally occurring examples) in which the child must make a decision about only one variable (e.g., how to interrupt an adult versus child). In time, additional choice indicators are included until complicated situations are constructed (e.g., a well-known adult is engaged in important but loud activity, and the child has urgent question to ask; a lesson that started as a lecture but has evolved into class discussion). The objective for this phase is for the child to make a decision based on the variables present in the scenario and to choose those skill elements that appear most fitting.

- Changing the choice of interrupting skill based on the situation.

The second part of this phase adds further complication to skill element utilization because in some situations, additional decisions need to be made concerning the use of interruption skill elements—for example, if a child, while still needing to interrupt, needs to tone it down or boost it up; or if the attempt to interrupt is rebuffed, whether to try again immediately, try again later, or forego the interruption.

Some examples are provided here:

- An adult on the phone has not responded to the child's attempt to convey an important message.
- Peers looked very annoyed when the child tried to talk over them to join in and the peers are not most preferred.
- A familiar, preoccupied adult has not responded to proximity and waiting and the question needs to be answered within the hour.
- When the two people talking paused, the child tried to interrupt and join in and ask a question, but the others just resumed chatting.

Commentary

It was determined by Sam's team that the frequency of interruptions he displayed, in addition to the manner of interruption incidents, was of concern. A phase was added that addressed not only how he interrupted, but how much he interrupted.

PHASE 7: Frequency of Interrupting. Using appropriate skills to interrupt may not be the only need demonstrated by a child. The child may need to regulate how often or much he or she interrupts. This adjustment may depend partially on the reactions of the other people involved. If the people being interrupted are getting annoyed by the frequency of interruptions, then it's time to tone it down. It may also depend on the setting and the extent to which the interrupting is disrupting or interfering with the activities involved. In general, frequency of interruption pertains not only to interruptions within a single conversation, but also to interruptions of the same person or within the same setting over a number of days or weeks.

Discrimination training should occur around the reactions of others, over time when a sequence of interruptions has occurred. Signs of annoyance or frustration in others (e.g., rolling eyes, sighing, frequent statements by a parent to "stop interrupting and let other people have a turn") should be included with repeated occurrences. Further, the child should be taught to anticipate what the likely reaction would be if he or she continues to interrupt after a period where frequent interruption had already occurred (e.g., "What do you think might happen if they were interrupted again?" or "Do you think she'll be happy to hear an interruption again?").

Additional discrimination work should involve noting when certain levels of interruption begin to interfere with the performance of certain tasks and activities in a range of settings. This effort can be combined with work that was done in Phase 3, teaching that in some circumstances even a small amount of interrupting is inappropriate.

Commentary

As with any skill, transfer of the interrupting skill to real-life conditions is essential. The team, recognizing that mastery truly requires generalization, adds that component to Sam's curriculum.

PHASE 8: Generalization. Although skill instruction has occurred in increasingly complex fashion, this phase involves transfer to naturally occurring situations. Effort needs to be directed at ensuring that the child can utilize his skills and knowledge of interrupting in real life. Chapter 2 of this book describes generalization protocols. In addition, the following areas should be considered as work moves the child from contrived training to everyday, naturally occurring situations:

- From familiar and preferred individuals to less known or preferred individuals
- From comfortable, familiar situations to less familiar circumstances
- From priming to no prior reminders or preparation

- From situations in which the interrupting interaction occurs in relative isolation to circumstances in which other activities are occurring simultaneously
- From neutral content areas to more important or urgent (to the child) matters
- From simple, straightforward situations requiring interrupting to those with several, possibly conflicting variables and indicators
- From more responsive and supportive reactions to interruption to less receptive or even antagonistic responses

Commentary

This example was designed to provide some insight into the way task and strategic analyses are created from scratch, and about the course of curriculum development. In a way, the process is like an inverted pyramid: It starts broadly and gradually works down to the needs of the individual child. Both instructional content and instructional strategy are part of the process. Much is guided by the development of clear objectives. Developing sufficient content and a clear, facilitative course to establish complete and authentic capabilities is essential.

The curriculum development process is not a static one, as we are constantly upgrading curricula and modifying them for the unique needs of individual children. The program written for Sam can certainly be used for other children (we deliberately chose not to use his name in the program and have included it in the Curriculum section of this book). However, doing so will likely require adaptation based on the particular needs of other children. Further, and as previously noted, the array and scope of social skills deficits in ASD are extensive; there are always new skills to tackle. The intention, therefore, is that this chapter, along with the examples provided in the Curriculum section of the book, will assist in the development of curricula for a broad range of social competencies, distinctly tailored and specifically designed for each unique individual with ASD.

8

The Social Skills Taxonomy Explained

Mitchell Taubman

Given the range and breadth of social skill deficits present in autism spectrum disorder (ASD), developing an exhaustive curriculum on social skills for individuals with ASD would be nearly impossible. It would truly need to be encyclopedic in length and scope. Moreover, most social skills curricula currently available either deal with the most basic social skills (e.g., eye contact, greetings, good-byes) or are designed to teach prosocial skills to antisocial children. These curricula have limited (at best) usefulness for children with ASD.

The social skills curriculum that follows this chapter has several guiding objectives. First, it is intended to help fill the void existing in social skills curriculum for individuals with ASD. Second, it is designed to provide a framework for teaching social skills, to give a sense of which areas need to be targeted to comprehensively address social issues. Third, it is intended to provide samples of programs in a range of areas, thereby offering examples for the development of additional, individualized social skills targets (see Chapter 7). Finally, the curriculum provides an array of specific programs addressing basic, intermediate, and advanced skills in a variety of "need areas" for individuals with ASD.

To assist in the presentation of the social skills curriculum, as well as to assist in social skills programming in general, a *social skills taxonomy* is offered here as the framework for social skills assessment, program development, and intervention. It should be noted that this taxonomy is merely a framework: It is not found in nature, and the areas it includes are overlapping and not mutually exclusive. Alternative conceptualizations are easy to imagine. The taxonomy in this chapter is provided as a way to assist understanding and to facilitate efforts geared at addressing (and assessing—see Chapters 6 and 7 of this book) this critical, challenging, and sometimes overwhelming learning and skill area.

The Social Skills Taxonomy

In ASD, needs in the social area can be substantial.[98] Even with an individual with high capabilities, deficits in social skills—from basic to complicated—may be present. Further, great unevenness and variability in social functioning may be displayed, with some abilities missing that might seem to be much simpler than advanced skills that are easily performed. Trying to gain an organized grasp and working sense of what is going on and what to do about social skills can be extremely challenging.

The social skills taxonomy has been developed to help in getting one's head and hands around social competency issues in work with individuals with ASD. It can help organize, categorize, and direct thinking and efforts. Fairly intuitive in structure and concept, it is designed so that most all social skills would be covered by at least one of the domains of the taxonomy. Areas included in this taxonomy are similar to, though independent from, other social skills concepts and frameworks.[22, 81]

The social skills taxonomy consists of five areas, each containing basic, intermediate, and advanced skills:

- Social Awareness
- Social Communication
- Social Interaction
- Social Learning
- Social Relatedness

As stated previously, there can be overlap between the areas, and the skills in the various areas are often interrelated. Such is the nature of social skills. A description of each area of the taxonomy follows.

SOCIAL AWARENESS

The Social Awareness area consists of the discrimination and understanding of social cues. It represents a rather substantial area of need for persons with ASD.[25,75,81,126] It can include being aware of social cues in the immediate social situation, recognizing social communication signals, sensing the internal world of another, and understanding the workings and interplay of surrounding social networks. It does not include the individual's actions in response to these cues (those actions are covered in another area), but rather encompasses just the identification and understanding of those cues.

Development of skills and understanding in this area typically occurs by such instructional means as matching, receptive labeling, or expressive labeling discriminations (see Leaf and McEachin's *A Work in Progress*[65] for explanations of these programs). Cues range from simple and obvious (basic) through extremely subtle and complex phenomena (intermediate- and advanced-level cues). Teaching may begin with simple discrimination (for example, receptive labeling of individuals in the child's immediate social world), progress to intermediate social reads (such as the impact of one's behavior on others), and finally proceed to advanced skills (actually taking the perspective of others).

Other targets in the Social Awareness area include awareness of the presence of others, labeling emotions, relationship identification, social rules, gestures, inferences/subtleties, understanding jokes, and theory of mind.

SOCIAL
COMMUNICATION

The Social Communication area is concerned with the social aspects of communication.[13, 51, 109] It involves all aspects of social communication—for example, verbal and nonverbal expression; what is said and how it is said; direct and implied conversation; figurative and literal speech; serious, sarcastic, and humorous statements; and tone, inflection, emphasis, and style.

Speech and language professionals often refer to the realm of social communication as "pragmatics." In fact, some of these same professionals might take the position that all social interaction is communicative. That is one theory, but there is an alternative perspective: Some aspects of social interchange are *not* communicative in nature, and those aspects may be the most important parts. For example, a person may have to make a social decision and then act on it; actual communication may play a minimum role in this process. Further, it is likely some social behavior has no communicative intent at all. Therefore, skills in the Social Communication area are those where the aspects are specifically and mainly communicative.

The Social Communication area includes basic conversation skills (see Leaf and McEachin's *A Work in Progress*[65] for additional description of these programs) such as simple greetings. Content in this area progresses to intermediate skills such as appropriate interrupting, on-topic conversation, and the nature, tone, and rhythm of conversations. Programs eventually move to advanced communication skills, such as sarcasm. Other targets in this area include simple question asking, open-ended question answering, giving compliments, providing feedback, apologizing, maintaining the flow of conversation, implying/subtlety, telling (funny) jokes, and expressing thoughts and feelings.

SOCIAL
INTERACTION

Skills in the Social Interaction area go beyond the conversational aspect of social behavior to address the process passing between individuals. This area focuses on teaching the skills necessary to be successful in social interchanges.[42, 50, 57, 97] Targets in this area often include conversational components, but the most important aspects involve the interactional process. These skills become especially important as children grow older and interactions become more sophisticated, layered, and complex. By middle school age, many of these targets could aptly be referred to as "survival skills."

This area includes basic skills (being in the proximity of others and responding to their initiations), intermediate skills (such as initiating and maintaining play interactions), and advanced abilities (such as social problem solving). Other targets in the Social Interaction area include waiting your turn, basic play participation, responding to cues, interactional reciprocity (e.g., not dominating the interaction), helping, assertion, negotiating, decision making, and coping.

SOCIAL
LEARNING

The Social Learning area is concerned with a child's ability to learn from and be influenced by his or her social environment.[20,34,69,87] Social Learning might not be thought of as an area of social competency; many of the targets in this area, related to observational learning, can be considered "learning how to learn" skills, for example. However, skills in this area are certainly part of the complex network of abilities contributing to an individual's social success. Social learning skills involve direct acquisition of social competency from peers through a variety of avenues, including direct imitation (live and in the moment), video modeling, and learning from pictorial sources. However, social learning capacities might also include indirect and incidental susceptibility to social influence and peer culture.

Social learning represents a means for acquiring new social skills. At the same time, targets in this area form a means for connection and responsiveness to those around a child, as well as to the social world and culture surrounding the child. Although related to social awareness skills, social awareness skills are not always a prerequisite to social learning because some social learning can occur outside of the individual's awareness (e.g., some aspects of peer culture can "rub off" on a child without the child noticing).

This area includes basic skills, such as early observational learning ("Copy her" or "Do that") as well as intermediate targets, such as vicarious learning (learning from the consequences that another person experiences). It also includes advanced skills (such as becoming receptive to peer influence).

Other targets in this area include nonverbal imitation (NVI), incidental learning, information seeking, availability to group process (getting swept away along with other kids by a group-wide effect, such as silliness, one-upmanship, the amplifying effects of group laughter), and learning to screen negative peer influence.

SOCIAL RELATEDNESS

The Social Relatedness area is concerned with the affective, connected, and relational aspect of social behavior. It involves the intent and desire behind social interactions and the essence and true purpose (not just action) of social competency. In a sense, it encompasses going through the emotions—not just the motions—of social behavior. It further is concerned with those elements of sociability, beyond standard social "skills," that are necessary for social connection and for authentic and successful friendships.[4,125,129]

Many have accused behaviorists of being insufficiently concerned with issues such as emotions, intent, and connectedness. Others say applied behavior analysis (ABA) is not applicable when attempting to address such phenomena. Unfortunately, the first statement is likely true. Fortunately, the second is not. An evolved, nonrigid ABA approach is up to the task. Such a contemporary ABA approach would be inclined to not only instill skills, but also ensure that the essence, intent, emotional content, and desire behind such skills are preserved and transmitted in the process. At the same time, a contemporary ABA model, by definition, would be systematic and programmatic in its approach to social skills intervention. It is clear that being systematic and programmatic is essential for success in the social area for children with ASD.[91]

Targets in the Social Relatedness area are often elusive, difficult to distill, subtle, and complicated. Therapists and teachers must be careful when working in this area. It can be easy to focus on behaviors that seem to address the social skills issue, but that actually create only an appearance of change and growth. It is all too often the case that interventionists address overt behavior but neglect the heart of the skill deficit—that is, the finer, underlying, affective aspects that are more difficult to address. Programs in this area need to connect with the deeper content, purpose, and essence of the targets. For this reason, curricula in this area are often sophisticated and complex, with nuanced elements. Although a critical variable may seem difficult to pin down, it will not be effectively established within an individual with ASD through unclear, ill-defined, obscure, or "magical" approaches. As in any truly effective treatment, those important social elements, no matter how subtle, need to be identified and instilled via solid programmatic effort. Therefore, the complex variables and skills that make up this area must be broken down and taught in a manner that allows for structured, systematic effort, yet at the same time is careful not destroy the targets' intent and essence.

The common denominator among the skills in the Social Relatedness area is the aspect of social connection. Skills in the area range from basic targets, such as development of peers' reinforcement value, to intermediate targets, such as social referencing and joint attention, to advanced ones, such as true empathy.

Other targets in this area include basic social interest, developing desire for proximity, engagement, affiliations/attachments, authentic friendships, interpersonal reciprocity (e.g., the balance of "give and take" in a relationship), compassion/caring, and altruism.

A Social Skills Framework

The objective, in sum total, of the social skills taxonomy is to provide a classification tool. This framework can assist at many levels, including in assessment work, for the development of instructional content, and in programmatic effort. In fact, in the Curriculum section of this book, we utilize this taxonomy as a means for organizing the programs that are presented there.

Like any tool however, the taxonomy is offered in service of a larger effort. As a construct, it is merely designed to support the instructional and programmatic content that forms the lion's share of this book. Such content constitutes the core of effective and successful social skills intervention for persons with ASD.

A SOCIAL SKILLS CURRICULUM FOR INDIVIDUALS WITH ASD

Mitchell Taubman
Julia Peacock
Julide Saltuklaroglu
Marlene Driscoll
Andrea Waks
Karen McKinnon
Jon Rafuse
Ron Leaf

The Social Skills Curricula

The following programs constitute a social skills curriculum for individuals with autism spectrum disorder (ASD). They are divided into and/or referenced to the areas of the social skills taxonomy (see Chapter 8). These programs are provided not only as specific instructional curricula, but as exemplars for further efforts focused on developing meaningful, individualized social skills instructional programs (see Chapter 7 on curriculum development). Within each of the domains of the taxonomy, a range of programs are offered, representing beginning, intermediate, and advanced competencies.

Each program includes the prerequisites for instruction in the area as well as the program's objectives. The individual curricula are divided into steps or phases, so that when applied the content can guide the progression of instruction. Many programs can be used in tandem with others. In fact, some may be most effective when integrated with others.

Of course, this curriculum is merely a guidebook; it is certainly not all-inclusive. Each individual with ASD is unique, and movement through specific programs as well as the entire curriculum will very much be an individualized matter. For some individuals, certain phases of some programs will be irrelevant; for others, intermediate steps will be necessary. Some individuals will power through programs; others will complete only the beginning steps of one or two targets. For some children, only a few of the programs provided here will be applicable or necessary. For others, a considerable number will be utilized and will be employed in conjunction with many additional individually tailored targets. The intent is that this social skills curriculum will be customized to fit each unique person with ASD. The hope is that it guides and assists the important efforts of professionals and parents in this critically important and uniquely challenging life area.

Under the framework of the social skills taxonomy, the following programs are provided (with information on cross-referencing to other taxonomy areas included):

Social Awareness

Social Categories
Relationship Identification
"How Do I Act In This Place?"
"People Don't Always Mean What They Say"
Perspective Taking (Theory of Mind)
Identifying Character Traits

Social Communication

Giving Compliments
Asking for Help and Soliciting Favors (cross-reference: Social Interaction)
Apologizing (cross-reference: Social Interaction)
Arguing, Discussing, Persuading, and Letting Go
"Go with the Flow" (Flow of Conversation)

Social Interaction

Responsiveness
Initiating Social Contact and Interaction
Play: Reciprocity and Flow
"Who Do You Choose?" (Choosing Peers for Social Interaction) (cross-references: Social
  Awareness; Social Relatedness)
Being a Good Sport
Responding to Teasing and Bullying
Interrupting Others (cross-reference: Social Communication)
Gaining Attention Through Problem Solving ("If at First You Don't Succeed, Try, Try Again")
Secrets (cross-references: Social Awareness; Social Relatedness)
Sharing (cross-references: Social Communication; Social Relatedness)

Social Learning

Social Imitation
Information Seeking (cross-references: Social Communication; Social Interaction)
Flow of Group Social Play (Stay with/Follow a Friend)
Vicarious Learning
Group Affiliation and Social Influence (cross-reference: Social Relatedness)

Social Relatedness

Tolerating the Presence and Proximity of Peers
Joint Attention II
Peer Social Interest and Engagement
Being a Good Friend (cross-references: Social Communication; Social Interaction)
Caring Responses and Empathy (cross-references: Social Awareness; Social Interaction)

SOCIAL
AWARENESS

Social Categories

Objectives

- Increase social awareness
- Develop age-appropriate interests and behaviors
- Increase social opportunities for the student
- Build skills necessary for social decision making

Prerequisites

- Social awareness★
- General knowledge and reasoning★
- Categories★

★See *A Work in Progress.*

Procedure

This program is designed to teach the student to identify and engage in age-appropriate activities and behavior. Initially, the student learns to identify relevant social categories and people who fall within them. It is important to focus on building knowledge of those categories that are most relevant to the individual student. Phases 1 and 2 can be presented using both visual and verbal strategies, as detailed next. The choice of teaching strategy will vary according to the needs of the individual student. Phases 3 through 6 involve applying that knowledge of age-appropriate activities and behavior to the environment, through making increasingly independent choices.

PHASE 1: Identify groups. The student learns to identify different categories of age groups (e.g., babies, toddlers, little kids, teenagers, grown-ups) and social groupings (e.g., males versus females, freshmen versus seniors, jocks versus computer-clubbers).

Step 1: Match photos to category labels

Step 2: Receptive identification
Example instructions:

- "Find a picture of a teenager."
- "Who is your age?"

Step 3: Expressive identification
Example instructions:

- "Name a little kid you know."
- "Tell me a grown-up TV star."

PHASE 2: Identify activities and behaviors. Teach the student to identify activities and behaviors appropriate to different age and social groups (include types of entertainment, leisure activities, conversation topics, clothing, play activities, language style, and behavior). Activities and behavior will vary based on the location where the student lives in and may change over time.

To increase independence in this skill, the student could be responsible for generating a list of variables or items to categorize. If possible, the student should explain how he or she got information to make these decisions ("I saw a commercial for it while watching a cartoon"; "I see kids at school wearing it"; "I listened to adults talking about it").

Step 1: Match pictures or objects to age or social group—for example, ballet to girls; the Dora figure to little kids; holding hands with a parent to little kids; Brad Pitt to teenage girls or grown-up women; saying "What's up?" with a teenager; meeting friends in the evening without grown-ups to older teenagers; knitting to grown-ups.

Step 2: Receptive identification
Example instructions:

- "Show me what a little kid wears."
- "Who rides in the cart at the grocery store?"
- "Pretend you are an (age/gender category) and find a game to play on the computer or a show to watch on TV."

Step 3: Expressive labeling
Example instructions:

- "Tell Santa what you want for Christmas (based on the group you fall in)."
- "Choose a song a little kid would like."
- "What are some things teenagers get to do that little kids can't do?"
- "What games would you play if you were a jock?"

Step 4: Role-play

- Role-play people from different groups having a conversation or engaging in free-time activities.
- At random times (e.g., when a timer beeps), the child must switch to a different category of person (from a little kid to a teenager).

PHASE 3: Apply knowledge in the teaching setting. The student learns to apply knowledge of age-appropriate activities and behaviors during teaching sessions. Initially, direct instruction may need to be used (e.g., "Choose a DVD older boys like to watch"); however, less direct language should be used when possible ("Oh, there seems to be lots of things here little girls like").

Step 1: Given a selection of toys and activities, the student should choose an age-appropriate option.

Step 2: During play dates or small-group sessions, the student should select age-appropriate conversation topics and use appropriate language style (visual prompting strategies could be used if necessary).

PHASE 4: Make independent choices. The student learns to independently select an activity or engage in behavior appropriate to his or her age or social group. Opportunities must be created to ensure the child is able to practice independent selection or demonstrate the targeted activities and behaviors.

For example:

- On a shopping trip, the child selects age-appropriate clothing.
- At the park, the student chooses leisure activities that other children his or her age would play.

PHASE 5: Make ongoing choices. Throughout the day, the student makes choices appropriate to his or her age and social group across a broad range of activities and behavior.

Relationship Identification

Objectives

- Increased ability to discriminate the different roles people fill in a student's life
- Increased awareness of personal relationships
- Improved safety awareness skills
- Increased awareness of appropriate versus inappropriate behaviors when interacting with others
- Reduction of potential vulnerability by practicing assertiveness skills
- Identification of which people to approach when in need of any level of assistance

Prerequisite Skills

- Assertiveness
- "I don't know"★
- General knowledge of community helpers
- Discrimination of strangers versus familiar people
- Social awareness★
- Categories★
- Matching★
- Receptive labeling★
- Expressive labeling★

★See *A Work in Progress.*

Procedure

Select the teaching strategy appropriate to the student's skill level.

The initial two program phases focus on teaching discrimination (of people in the student's life; of roles those people may fill; of responsibilities consistent with those roles; and so on). Using photographs can assist in this teaching. Present pictures depicting different people, and teach the student to identify each individual. Further, teach the student to identify the category (or the circle of intimacy) those people belong in, and to define the roles each circle encompasses.

Individualize the categories to ensure they are relevant and meaningful to the student. Age-appropriate terminology should be used for the category names.

Phases 3 through 5 involve teaching about appropriate behavior with others, given their category in relationship to the student. Specific scenarios, role-plays, and opportunities to rehearse with people in the natural environment are used to practice applying the knowledge gained in earlier phases.

As prompts, provide photographs, a visual representation of the circles of intimacy (see the basic example at the end of this program activity) or other visual strategies (e.g. cards with category labels).

PHASE 1: Receptive and expressive identification of all individuals from an array of photos or pictures. Teach student to categorize people based on the relationship that person has with the student. Categories include, but are not limited to, the following:

- Family
- Friends
- Teachers or other professionals
- People who help you (e.g., police, doctors)
- Acquaintances and people you don't know very well
- Absolute strangers

These categories can be represented with circles of intimacy, as a category list, or by grouping photos or names together.

Step 1: Matching/categorization

- The student sorts picture or photos to the category names.

Step 2: Receptive identification

- The student demonstrates understanding by indicating to the teacher (by pointing, giving, or some other behavior) the category in which a person belongs.
- Example instructions:
    - "Which one of these people is in your family?"
    - "Show me the circle your brother is in."

Step 3: Expressive labeling

- The student demonstrates comprehension by verbally naming/labeling the appropriate category for each person, or names people within a category.
- Example instructions:
    - "Can you tell me someone who is in your family?"
    - "Who are some friends?"
    - "What relationship is (teacher's name) to you?"

PHASE 2: Teach student to describe the traits defining each category or circle. Have the student provide several descriptive attributes for each category/circle.

Step 1: Matching

- Have the student match attributes to the corresponding category.

Step 2: Receptive identification

- Teach the student to point to the category or circle corresponding to a role description provided as an instruction by the teacher. For example:
  - "Show me people who live with you." (The student points to the "family" circle.)
  - "Which people come over to your house to play?" (The student points to the "friends" circle.)
  - "Your parents talk to these people, but you don't know them very well." (The student points to the "acquaintances" circle.)
  - "You can go to these people for help." (The student points to the "professionals/people who help you" circle.)

Step 3: Expressive identification

- Have the student expressively define the role each category encompasses. The definitions should be individualized to ensure they are specific and meaningful to the student. For example:

  - Family:

    - Someone related to you
    - Someone who lives with you

  - Friends:

    - Someone you like to spend time with
    - Someone who has some of the same interests you do
    - Someone in your class you like to talk with
    - A person in your Cub Scouts pack (or other extracurricular activity)
    - Someone who come over your house to play
    - People who play with you during recess
    - A person you hang out with when you have time

  - Professionals/people who help you:

    - People you go to if you need assistance
    - Someone you talk to if you are lost
    - A person you tell if you get hurt
    - Someone you call if you are threatened or bullied

  - People you don't know very well:

    - Someone you have played with one or two times
    - People you have seen your parents talk to, but you don't know
    - Someone in a different grade than you at school

- Absolute strangers:

  - Someone you have never seen before
  - People you have seen before but never talked to
  - People you don't know anything about
  - Someone whose name you may know, but don't play with
  - A friend of your friend (who you've never spent time with)

PHASE 3: Teach the "rules of interaction." Have the student identify appropriate behaviors relative to the category or circle of intimacy in which he or she belongs. Some behaviors may need to be finely discriminated (for example, different types of hugging or touching). The following are examples of possible behaviors:

- Who do you hug?
- Who do you give your address to?
- Who do you go to the movies with?
- Who do you kiss?
- Who do you invite to your house?
- Who do you go to when you're lost?
- Who do you talk to when you need help?
- Who do you hold hands with?
- Who do you say "Hi" to?
- Who do you let into your house?
- Who do you go to when you get hurt?
- Whose car can you get into?
- Who would you get a ride home from school with?

Step 1: Matching

- Teach the student to place a written description of behavior with the category name.

Step 2: Receptive identification

- Teach the student to point to the category name(s) or circle(s) of intimacy appropriate to the stated behavior. For example:

  - "Show me who it's okay to say 'Hi' to."

Step 3: Expressive identification

- Teach the student to name the correct category (or provide the correct answer) based on a specified descriptor. For example:
  - "Tell me who you can get a ride home from school with."
  - "Who can touch you where your bathing suit covers?"

- "Is it okay to kiss your Mom?" ("yes" or "no")
- "Is it okay to tell your friend that your parents got in a fight last night?" ("yes" or "no")

PHASE 4: Present the student with social scenarios involving people from different relational categories. The student learns to describe the appropriate actions or responses to make based on the relationship. Scenarios can be provided verbally or in written form. Initially, having a list of options from which the student may select and verbalize to you may be helpful. Some instructional examples follow:

- "You are at the supermarket and you see your cousin running over to hug you. What do you do?"
- "You are at the park, and a stranger smiles at you and then asks for your help. What should you do?"
- "You are at a public library and you see your teacher. What could you do?"

PHASE 5: Role-play social scenarios involving people in different relationship categories. The student should engage in appropriate behavior based on the relationship. Some instructional examples follow:

- "Let's pretend I'm your teacher and I see you at the mall."
- During the role-play, the teacher offers the student a ride home. Have the student demonstrate appropriate responses.

PHASE 6: Create real-life situations under naturalistic conditions to provide opportunities to practice and apply mastered concepts. Prompting in the form of modeling or priming may be necessary initially. It may be important to address responding appropriately when inappropriate initiations are made by strangers, but it will be essential at some stage to randomize opportunities created with people in different relationship categories. Some opportunities include the following:

- Offer a ride
- Ask for the student's address
- Ask for the student's telephone number
- Try to enter the student's house
- Call on the telephone
- Offer the student food or toys
- Ask the student to follow you
- Ask to use the bathroom in the student's house

PHASE 7: Help the student understand that over time, individuals may move from one category to another. For example:

- An acquaintance can become a friend
- A friend you rarely see anymore can become an acquaintance
- Certain family members may become unsafe

A Representation of Relational Categories (Squares of Intimacy)

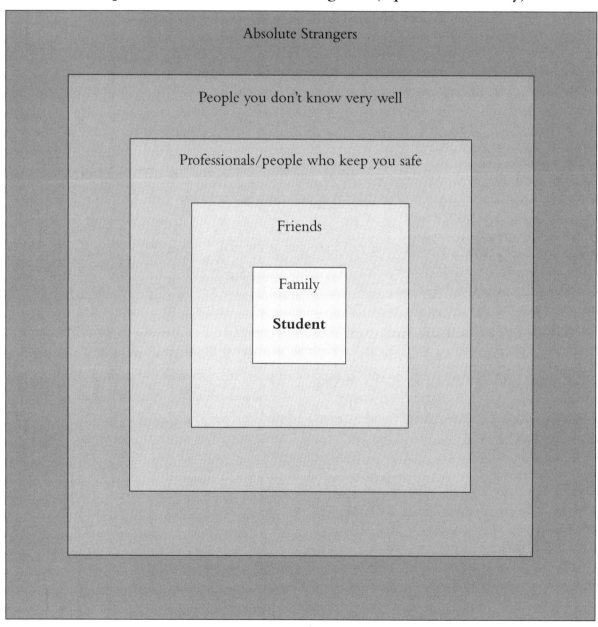

How Do I Act In This Place?

Objectives

- Enhance social problem-solving skills
- Generalize setting-appropriate behavior
- Increase ability to rely on multiple resources
- Increase awareness of the complexity of cues in social situations
- Facilitate greater independence

Prerequisites

- Observational and vicarious learning skills★
- Basic environmental awareness skills★
- Independent information-seeking skills
- Inferences
- Joint attending
- Social desire

★See *A Work in Progress.*

Procedure

This program involves a series of discrimination exercises and follow-up instructional sessions. Although instruction will initially involve carefully contrived arrangements, later generalization will be essential for application of skills in challenging, naturalistic situations.

PHASE 1: Initial discrimination. The student learns that some settings and locations are associated with specific, customary forms of conduct and behavior. Further, the student is taught common guidelines and implicit rules of behavior and conduct customary to a number of settings, including the following locations:

Libraries	Hospitals	Physician waiting rooms
Museums	Movie theaters	Funerals
Restrooms	Hotels	Concerts
Sporting events/games	Malls	Gyms

PHASE 2: Observe others. The student learns to determine the rules of behavior for a novel setting by observing the behavior of other individuals in that setting. Start with settings (for example, a convenience store) that typically have few people and that contain obvious, common routines and responding demands. Gradually move to larger, more complicated locations (such as a playground or a swap meet).

PHASE 3: Infer rules of conduct from the setting. The student learns to infer rules of conduct from the setting itself and indirectly from the behavior of individuals in that setting. Start with settings where conduct hints are obvious (such as a bus station with loads of available seating). Over time, move to settings where behavior clues are more subtle (for example, in a buffet or cafeteria setting where stacks of trays indicate where to begin the self-serve process).

PHASE 4: Synthesize informational cues. The student learns to combine all cues and synthesize all methodologies for determining appropriate behaviors in naturally occurring situations. The student learns to ask for assistance (and who to ask depending on the setting—for example, store employees, receptionists, information desks, self-help kiosks). It is most preferable that the student attempts all avenues to independently assess and respond to the individual setting before asking someone for help. Asking for assistance can be an inhibitor to greater self-reliance—especially when help is not truly required—and should be taught as a last resort.

"People Don't Always Mean What They Say"

Objectives

- Increase general social awareness
- Teach recognition that meaning derives not only from spoken words, but also from phraseology and body language
- Increase understanding that combinations of multiple communicative modes and forms (including spoken words, facial expression, gestures, vocal tone, contextual cues, and body language) work together to convey meaning
- Increase critical evaluative skills to better understand communication and spoken messages
- Promote comfort, confidence, and appropriate emotional response to subtle communication

Prerequisite Skills

- Recognizing facial expressions★
- Cause and effect★
- Discriminating vocal tone
- Understanding gestures and body language★
- Inferences (basic)
- Understanding absurdities/incongruities (basic)

★See *A Work in Progress.*

Procedure

Teach each aspect of nonverbal communication separately. The order can be varied according to the individual student's needs or abilities.

PHASE 1: The student learns to identify specific communicative components so as to evaluate and better understand the intended meaning of a communication. These components include the following:

- Facial expressions (what the communicator's face looks like)
- Intonation (how the communicator's voice sounds)
- Body language or gestures (how the communicator's body looks and moves)
- Context (what is happening in a background or surrounding sense)
- Statement content (what was actually said)

PHASE 2: When the student is presented with a statement and one other aspect of communication (from the previously mentioned components), the student should indicate whether the two aspects are compatible, and why. For example:

- "I'm so happy." (Looks mad)
- "This is lots of fun." (Rude tone)
- "I'm so full." (After a big meal)
- "You're bad." (When giving you a high five)

PHASE 3: When the student is presented with a statement and two other aspects of communication, the student should indicate which of the aspects are compatible, and why.

PHASE 4: All aspects of communication are included in the statement presented to the student. The student indicates the intended meaning of the communication.[†]

PHASE 5: The student indicates the intended meaning of a communication presented within a role-play scenario and/or video clips.

PHASE 6: The student learns to identify specific types of communication that include multiple facets to convey meaning. For example:

- Sarcasm
- Teasing
- Exaggeration
- Joking
- Statements with more than one meaning

PHASE 7: After observing real-life, naturally occurring situations, the student is able to identify the intended meaning and type of the communication.

[†]*The intensity and importance of any single communicative aspect/component may be considered in determining meaning, in addition to the quantity of various aspects that are congruent.*

Perspective Taking
(Theory of Mind)

Objectives

- Demonstrate an increased ability to attend to others
- Better understand that others have perspectives
- Learn that others may see, understand, think, feel, believe, or desire differently than one another and the student
- Understand and ascertain when others have knowledge or perspectives different than the student's
- Build the requisite skills for responding to others' perspectives
- Build the requisite skills for empathy

Prerequisite Skills

- Imaginative play★
- Joint attention★
- Comprehension★
- Receptive and expressive identification of emotions★
- Cause and effect (including how one comes to "know" something)★
- Recall★
- Environmental and social awareness★
- Inferences
- "People don't always mean what they say"
- Understanding the concept of perspective

★See *A Work in Progress.*

Procedure

The phases outlined here describe the process of teaching perspective-taking skills. Development of these abilities usually occurs in a specific sequence, so it may be necessary to teach most of the phases in the order in which they are outlined here, as mastery of one phase may be requisite before the student can fully comprehend the next phase.

Phase 1: Differing perspectives

Step 1: Differing vantage points
"What do you see?" "What does someone else see?"

- *Show a picture.* The teacher holds a picture of interest up. Set up the situation so that a number of people, including the student, are sitting in various places around the room.

Hold the picture so one person can see it, but not another. Ask the student, "Can (student 1) see the picture? Can (student 2) see the picture?" The student should discriminate who can see the picture based on who is oriented toward it. Turn the picture away from the student and ask, "Can you see the picture?"

- *Have the student show his or her own work.* The student should orient the page so the person can see it, rather than the student orienting it toward himself or herself. Place a number of people around the room. Tell the student, "Now show the picture to (student 3). Next, show it to (student 4)." The student should turn the picture, orienting it to each person's point of view.

- *Use objects and photographs of those objects to teach how something can look different depending on the point of view.* In this exercise, the student learns that two people may see the same object differently. Use known items and take photos of known objects having different attributes when viewed from different angles. For example, a toy car looks different when viewed from the front, the back, the side, from above, and from below. This is obviously also true with a chair, a doll, a teddy bear, a model airplane, or a doll house. For each object, take two or three photos from different angles. Start with items that provide dramatically different views from different angles.

  Place an object in the middle of a table. Place the student so he or she can see only one view of the object (e.g., the back of the car). Place a second person so they can see a different view of the object (e.g., the front of the car).

  Place all photos of the various angles in front of the student. Ask the student, "Which view do you see?" versus "Which view does (person 2) see?" This part of the exercise can be done expressively as well: "Who sees the front of the bus?" or "What does (person 2) see?"

- *Use objects within rooms to further demonstrate the concept.* Have the student stand in front of one object in the room. Have another person stand in front of another object. Each person is looking at the object in front of him or her. Teach the student to discriminate what can be seen in a room versus what someone is actually looking at.

  A further step: Have the student and a cohort walk to a different room. Once the pair are in the new room together, have the student return to the original room. Have the cohort stay in the different room (for example, initially the two were in the living room, and then both walked to the kitchen; the student returned to the living room, while the cohort stayed in the kitchen). Offer photos of objects from each room for the student to choose from. Ask the student, "Can (cohort) see this?" The student should discriminate what he or she thinks the cohort might be able to see, based on the room that person is in. For example, the cohort might be able to see the refrigerator, but cannot see the television in the living room.

- *Use a blocked view.* Set up a situation in which a small item (e.g., a toy car) is blocked from view by a larger item (e.g., a partition). Have a person look in the direction of the car. Ask the student, "Can (person 1) see the car?" The answer is "no," even when the person is looking in the direction of the object. Move the box away and ask the same question. The answer is now "yes," because the person can indeed see the object. The student is learning to discriminate between a blocked view—even if the student can see the object, that doesn't mean the other person can—and a view that is no longer blocked—now both parties can see the object.

Step 2: What the student knows versus what someone else knows

- Set up a variety of situations involving a range of sensory modalities. Have the student observe someone doing a specific activity causing that person to "know" or learn something. For example, a friend watches as his mother takes a cake from the refrigerator and puts it on the table. Ask the student, "Does (your friend) know the cake is on the table?" The student should answer "yes." Then ask, "How does (your friend) know?" The answer is, "because (the friend) saw her put it there."
- The student learns to discriminate between things he or she knows versus things another person knows. The student may learn a number of discriminations:

  - The student knows, but the other person does not know
  - The other person knows, but the student does not know
  - Both the student and the other person know
  - Both the student and the other person do not know
  - The other person does not know, and the student knows the other person doesn't know
  - The other person knows, and the student knows the other person knows
  - The other person does not know, and the student does not know the other person doesn't know
  - The other person knows, and the student does not know the other person knows

Example 1
The student and the other person go to separate rooms and perform an action written down in each room. After performing the action, both return to the teacher. Ask the student, "Do you know what (person) did?" and "Does (person) know what you did?"

Example 2
Person 1 and the student go outside to play soccer, where person 1 kicks the ball over the fence. Person 2 stays inside to watch TV. Ask the student, "Does (person 1) know the soccer ball went over the fence?" and "How does he know?" Also ask, "Does (person 2) know the ball went over the fence?" and "Why not?" The answer to the last question is "because Person 2 did not see the action occur."

Example 3

The student receives an award at school assembly. The student's mother did not attend the ceremony. Ask the student, "Does your mom know what you got at assembly today?" and "Why not?" Then ask, "Does your teacher know?" and "How does she know?"

Example 4

A person looks into a bag to see an object within. The student does not watch this action. Ask the student, "Do you know if (person) knows what's in the bag?" (The answer is "no.") As a contrast, the student then watches the person look into the bag. Ask the same question (the answer is now "yes").

Phase 2: Identify desire

Step 1: "What is important to you?"

- Provide the student with a worksheet listing 15–20 desires common to all of us. Have the student indicate how important each desire is (low, medium, or high interest level). It is helpful to stress that a middle ground exists for individuals with regard to preference of desires and that preference is typically not an all-or-nothing proposition. Desires may include the following:

  - Control
  - Family time
  - Sports
  - Learning new things
  - Eating
  - Fame
  - Getting good grades
  - Acceptance
  - Video games
  - Power
  - Popularity

  For younger children, listing tangible items or familiar games and activities may be more helpful with this lesson. Older children may better understand abstract concepts such as control or independence; if not, more understandable language can be used (e.g., "Being able to do things without help").

  Once the worksheet is completed, review the student's choices and compare them with those of other people. Explain that, for the most part, no two people will have exactly the same desire profile, and that is what makes us unique. The teacher may also have the student provide possible rationales for why another person would have high desire for an area the student indicated as a "low desire" and explain what the student's own rationales for his or her choices.

Step 2: Observing and assessing desire in others

- Determining what a person wants or desires is possible by simply asking or observing that individual. The student should observe a person who wants an object versus one who does not want the object. Have the person visually show he or she wants the item, or does not want it. Ask the student, "Does (the person) want the chips?" and "How do you know (the person) wants them?" or "How do you know (the person) doesn't want them?"

  How does someone demonstrate whether he or she has a preference for something? Some helpful hints to teach the student might include the following:

  - Does the person look at it?
  - Does the person reach for it?
  - Does the person ask for it?
  - If it is offered, does the person choose it?
  - Is the person happy when he or she gets it? (Smile, laugh, say something positive)
  - Does the person spend time with it?
  - Does the person talk about it?
  - Does the person do these things often when in the presence of it, rather than just once?

  Over time, the student can get to know what another person wants through observation. Knowing—or inferring—what a person wants by watching his or her actions can assist the student in understanding the person's general desires. This, in turn, can assist the student in interpreting intention based on the relevant actions and words someone uses.

Phase 3: Identify emotions ("affective perspective taking")

- Affective perspective taking refers to the ability to understand another person's emotions and feelings. Identifying another's emotions is described in detail in the Emotions program.
- It is important to teach the student how to interpret verbal and nonverbal cues about emotions. The student should learn to answer questions such as "How does she feel?" and "How do you know she feels sad/angry/happy?" or "Why is she sad?" The "People Don't Always Mean What They Say" program in this book would be useful here.

Phase 4: Identify thoughts and beliefs (What is someone else thinking?)

Step 1: Predicting what a person might be thinking

- Use pictures, videos, or role-plays to illustrate situations involving clear actions or events. Ask the student to determine what each person might be thinking. The student should base his or her answers on the knowledge and skills built from previous phases and requisite programs, including identifying nonverbal cues and the situation's context (e.g., setting, event, person's words, body language).

EXAMPLE SITUATIONS	POSSIBLE THOUGHTS
Child falls off bike, father nearby.	Child: "Ouch!" Father: "I hope he's okay."
Child walks onto road; another person is shouting out something.	Person: "Oh no, he's going to get hit by a car." Child: Thinking about getting to soccer practice on time.
Child is drawing on wall; mother is standing behind child with her hands on hips.	Mom: "You are in big trouble!" Child: "I am in big trouble!"
Peer has a box of old rotten fruit and says to friend, "Put your hand in here—I've got something for you."	Peer: "I'll trick him." Friend: "This is exciting."

Step 2: Sometimes others have different beliefs

- The student learns his or her beliefs may differ from those of others. Provide the student with many different examples where his or her own beliefs vary from the beliefs of others.

Example 1

Person 1 puts a hat on a table and walks away. Person 2 picks up the hat, puts it in Person 1's school bag, and then walks out. Person 3 takes the hat out of the bag and puts it under a bed. Ask the student, "Where does (Person 1) believe the hat is?" ("On the table") and "Where does Person 2 believe the hat is?" ("In the school bag").

Example 2

Show the student a box of chocolates in which the chocolates have been replaced by pencils. Have someone else (Person 1) enter the room and look at the closed box of chocolates. Ask the student, "What does (Person 1) think is inside the box?" and "What do you think is inside the box?"

Example 3

Hide an object in a box. Have the student and another person (Person 1) try to guess what is inside the box. Person 1 should indicate what he or she thinks is in the box (e.g., "Maybe it's a ball" or "It might be a donkey"). Right before the teacher discloses the answer, ask the student, "What do you think is inside the box?" and "What does (Person 1) think is inside the box?"

Step 3: Advanced perspective-taking effort

- In time, the student should learn that individuals may come away from the same event with differing beliefs (potentially based on different vantage points).
- Additionally, "second-order" belief can be addressed. Second-order beliefs occur when a person has a perspective about what someone else believes about another person's beliefs, thoughts, or feelings. For example, "The student believes Rick thinks Sally feels she won't get invited to the party."

- Further complexity can be added to perspective taking. For example, the student can learn that differing beliefs and values occur not just based on viewing the same event. Differing beliefs can also occur when two people hear the same content, topic, or issue. In addition, having read something, people can have different ideas about what the main idea is or what the perspective is.
- The student can learn that others' perspectives can change. Scenarios can be created in which events produce a change in another's perspective (thoughts, opinions, feelings, beliefs). The student can be asked to explain why the perspective changed or, based on the new occurrences, what the other person's perspective may now be.
- Finally, the student can work toward developing a better ability to infer intent, based on observing someone's actions, gestures, or body language. Essential elements of this level of perspective-taking effort include remembering and using specific situational context, having previous observational history, "knowing" the person whose actions are being evaluated, and a firm understanding of nonverbal cues.

Examples of Advanced Perspective-Taking Exercises

- **Giving Directions to Others**

  - Have the student guide you toward an item by giving instructions. Initially, the student may walk with you. Eventually, the student should be able to give directions from a stationary location and modify the instructions to suit the perspective of the accomplice.
  - Progress to the student giving directions based on memory. For example, if the student and an accomplice are watching television in the living room, have the student direct the accomplice to go to the kitchen (a different room) and retrieve sodas (the student does not have the benefit of being in the same room to watch the accomplice and modify the instructions).

- **Withholding Information**

  Games such as I Spy, Guess Who, Charades, and Kids on Stage are good options for teaching children to withhold information (teaching that "you know something and the other does not"). All of these games rely on the players' ability to hold back information and give meaningful clues without revealing the answer.

- **Practical Jokes, Magic Tricks, and Optical Illusions**

  Playing harmless pranks on other people can be a great way of understanding another person's perspective. For example, hide a toy snake in the pantry and prepare to ask another person to check there. Ask the student, "What does (person) think is in the cupboard?" and "What might (person) do happen when she sees the snake?"

  Many magic tricks also involve perspective taking. Objects that are placed in a magic hat often turn into to different things, so you can ask the student, "What does the magician think is in the hat?" and "What does the audience think is in the magic hat?"

Optical illusions or magic eye pictures, if different images can be perceived (emphasis prompts can sometimes be used to assist in this process), can also be fun and illustrate the possibility of multiple perspectives

- **Deception**

Developing an understanding of deception is another way to teach perspective taking. An added bonus may be the development of a student who is less naïve and gullible. In this sense, the goal would be generating an understanding that someone can actively create and promote an alternative perspective and direct it at another. A note of caution here: This activity would not mean explicitly teaching deception, but rather that examples of others' deception would be utilized as perspective-taking exercises. The focus here is the development of deception recognition. Monitoring for the potential adoption of deceptive practices should occur and, if necessary, would need to lead to additional skill instruction (e.g., on the importance of honesty).

Fairy tales such as those involving Snow White, the Gingerbread Man, and Little Red Riding Hood include themes of deception. These examples can be used to probe themes relating to deception. Questions such as "Who does Snow White think the lady is?", "Who is the lady, really?", "What do you think the wolf hopes to gain by dressing up as Granny?", and "Why did the witch dress up as a lady selling apples?" can guide the student to a better understanding of others' perspectives and motives.

Identifying Character Traits

Objectives

- develop the ability to make social judgments
- Establish a deeper and more reliable sense of others
- Develop authentic peer relationships
- Increase the likelihood of successful social interactions
- Develop decision-making and problem-solving skills
- Increase self-awareness
- Develop critical evaluation and thinking skills

Prerequisites

- Cause and effect★
- Extensive recall ability
- Inferences
- Relationship identification
- Social categories
- "People don't always mean what they say"
- "Who do you choose?"

★See *A Work in Progress.*

Procedure

Through instruction, individuals with ASD may be able to identify and become aware of the manner in which another person is acting (e.g., "She is being funny," "He is acting shy," "He made a great shot"). They may also come to recognize intention behind actions, even when conflicting information is present (see the Perspective Taking and "People Don't Always Mean What They Say" programs in this book). For example, another child may say she will not engage in bullying behavior anymore—but then turn around the next day and once again do so. The child with ASD can learn to discern and infer, "She didn't mean what she said."

It has been our experience, however, that a deeper understanding of others can be lacking in even those persons with ASD who have progressed far in therapy and have advanced social abilities. In regard to the examples mentioned in the preceding paragraph, they may not come to realize over time that a particular person is funny, that another is introverted, that a peer is athletic, or that another child (in addition to being a bully) cannot be trusted. In essence, they do not come to see character or personality traits and learn to operate in interactions and relationships accordingly. This section is designed to provide instruction in that area.

Work in this area should proceed with caution, as the intention is to avoid developing in the person with ASD stereotyping, pigeonholing, and profiling-type thinking. The student should also be taught that while traits may represent enduring characteristics based on consistency of history, they are not immutable: It is certainly possible that "a leopard can change its spots." The major function of teaching about traits is to help the child better predict behavior, more deeply understand the behavior of others, and, based on expectations, make choices and act accordingly.

In terms of students' stage of development, this program is not typically appropriate prior to early elementary school age.

PHASE 1: Common trait identification and discrimination. Video, pictorial, story, and in vivo examples of age- and culture-level typical traits are taught through exemplars. These can include the following traits:

Smart	Thoughtful	Dishonest
Funny	Athletic	Unpredictable
Mean	Unfair	Energetic
Bashful	Helpful	Loyal

Traits are taught through discrimination training. Examples should involve multiple episodes of behaviors (e.g., a child doing well on homework, passing a test, and giving the right answers in class; a child being deceptive about a variety of actions and situations to a parent, peer, and teacher). The child should learn that the consistent appearance of a behavior or characteristic amounts to a trait.

PHASE 2: Finer trait discrimination. Video, pictorial, and in vivo examples of traits versus mere behavioral episodes (including uncharacteristic performance) are presented. The intent is for the student to learn what is simply an episode of a type of action or behavior (e.g., not telling the truth; an atypical episode of temper) and what qualifies as a consistent pattern of action or performance (e.g., untrustworthiness; violent temperament) that would constitute a trait.

Further, examples where patterns of behavior are not unilateral—that is, when there are exceptions to common performance—should be presented to teach trait discernment under complex conditions (e.g., a child who is honest with his best friend, but not with anyone else; a student who is uncooperative when in a fussy mood only).

PHASE 3: Using traits to predict behavior. In this phase, stories, videos, and in vivo scenarios are utilized to illustrate a pattern of behavior for an individual as well as a presenting situation or circumstance that will require choice, statement, or action on the part of the individual. The student must predict, based on the historical pattern of behavior (trait), what the individual will do in the presenting situation. Typically, after making his or her prediction, the student can be shown the actual outcome.

Some scenario examples follow:

Pattern of Behavior ⟶ Presenting Situation

A child is funny at home and in the classroom	The child enters a birthday party
A child refuses to have a snack, swing on the swings, or stop bouncing a ball	The child is riding a bike and it is time to ask for your turn
A child is not given ice cream in the store, not allowed to cut to the front of the line, not permitted to cross the street by himself, and each time screams and falls to the floor	The child sees another child playing with a desired toy
A specific student assists a child in a wheelchair and helps the teacher carry something without being asked	Another student is hurt and there are a group of students nearby, including the specific student

Eventually the presenting situations should become more subtle in terms of how they may relate to the trait (sometimes they should not relate to the trait at all, thereby demonstrating that history may not, in many cases, provide relevant predictive information). Also, some presenting scenarios should show surprising information, illustrating that traits are not absolutely, irrefutably predictive (some should even depict individuals reliably "changing their ways").

PHASE 4: Making decisions based on traits. The child is taught to weigh a number of factors in understanding that what is decided or done in presenting situations may be affected by another person's traits. You can use scenarios similar to those used in Phase 3 for this phase. Factors employed in making trait-influenced decisions should include the following:

- Strength and consistency of the person's prior history
- Relationship of the presenting situation and the trait
- Alternatives and resources if trait-based behavior should appear
- Relative costs and benefits of approaching or avoiding the presenting situation

Actions and responses based on decisions (e.g., asking to share, requesting help, asserting oneself, getting teacher assistance, ignoring) should be practiced as well. However, prior teaching in such areas (see, for example, the Asking for a Favor, Discussing and Persuading, Accepting and Making Offers to Play, Teasing and Bullying, and Sharing programs in this book) may be necessary before this phase is attempted.

Included in this phase can be scenarios that involve choices the child must make, which potentially may be affected by traits (e.g., choosing who to play with [see "Who Do You Choose?"], who to do a work project with, who to tell a secret to [see "Secrets"]).

Care should be taken to move training in this phase from contrived scenarios into real-life, everyday situations. (See the discussion of generalization in Chapter 2.)

PHASE 5: Self-awareness and self-esteem. With success in the first four phases, work in this area could progress to promoting self-awareness as well as self-esteem. While the efforts described in this section are not intended to serve as a substitute for more comprehensive therapeutic work in such areas, the effort in Phase 5 can certainly be facilitative for children of high capabilities.

- To promote self-awareness, work in Phase 1 and Phase 2 would now be applied to the identification of personal patterns of behavior. While there may be some value in gaining a sense of one's own negative traits, it is recommended that work with children with ASD should begin and predominantly focus on awareness of positive personality traits and characteristics. Besides promoting general self-knowledge, such work can help an individual learn to "play to his or her strengths." If great success with awareness of positive self-traits is achieved, then focus on negative characteristics—albeit only to facilitate work on positively influencing such undesirable traits—can be included in limited fashion.

- With progress in establishing an individual's sense of personal traits, effort can be applied in the self-esteem area. A developed sense of positive self-characteristics can in and of itself contribute to self-esteem. However, gaining the understanding that some personal characteristics are enduring can help a children develop a more stable and firm sense of who they are and be an antidote to perfectionism and over-abundant self-criticism. When children learn that an action or episode is not self-defining, they tend to not be as hard on themselves. When they learn that who they are does not derive from a certain incident but instead from what they are about in an enduring (and positive) sense, they tend to be more satisfied with themselves. Having a deeper sense of who they are in a positive sense (and working on and building on those positive attributes) tends to produce more profound and authentic self-esteem.

SOCIAL
COMMUNICATION

Giving Compliments

Objectives

- Teach social conversational skills
- Promote interactional reciprocity
- Promote increased awareness of actions and emotions
- Increase acceptance by peers

Prerequisites

- Conversation skills (intermediate)★
- Cause and effect (basic)★

★See *A Work in Progress.*

Procedure

Depending on the student's skill level and ability set, Discrete Trial Teaching or Teaching Interactions may be used for various elements of the skill instruction.

PHASE 1: Discrimination training. While exposed to a contrived situation (either described or videotaped), the student is taught to discriminate whether a compliment is warranted. Situations warranting a compliment include the following:

- Witnessing someone achieve success
- Observing someone win a competition
- Hearing someone share a success
- Noticing that someone is dressed up
- Noticing that someone has tried to enhance his or her appearance
- Hearing someone say an item he or she is presenting or displaying was just purchased (e.g., showing a new car)
- After receiving a compliment

The student is subsequently taught which salient features of situations are worthy of compliments.

PHASE 2: The student learns to give a customary or common compliment. Be sure to practice the various compliment components, such as conversational content (e.g., "That was awesome," "Cool"), voice tone and inflection, facial expressions (e.g., smiles, looks of surprise), body language (e.g., leaning in, orienting toward the person), and other nonverbal communication (e.g., high fives, thumbs-up gestures). Try not to teach compliments in scripted fashion, but rather work on developing various forms of the same component.

PHASE 3: Applying compliment skills. The student applies acquired compliment skills in response to situations learned (or similar to those learned) in Phase 1.

Subsequently, the student learns to make more specific compliments, focusing on what is worthy of a compliment within the scenarios provided. Additionally, the student must learn how to specifically phrase the compliment, given the particular situations. For example:

- From general compliment: "You look nice." to specific compliment: "I really like your dress. Where did you get it?"

PHASE 4: In structured but in vivo situations, the student is taught to discriminate whether a compliment should be given. If a compliment is warranted, the student also evaluates which type of compliment is appropriate (see Phase 3) and delivers the compliment.

PHASE 5: Learning is generalized to naturalistic situations, including those in which compliment opportunities occur in intermittent and unpredictable fashion.

Asking for Help and Soliciting Favors

Objectives

- Increased ability to get needs met in a more age-appropriate fashion
- Increased independence
- Increased motivation to meet peers and develop relationships
- Increased peer reinforcement value
- Enhanced social interactions with others
- Increased ability to get needs and desires met
- Increased understanding of social reciprocity

Prerequisites

- Self-awareness (individualized understanding of strengths and weaknesses)
- Basic awareness of conduct
- Problem-solving skills
- Observational learning ability★
- Frustration tolerance skills
- "Asking questions"★
- Inference understanding (for Phase 3b)

★*See A Work in Progress.*

Procedure

This program teaches students both to ask for help and to solicit favors, in particular from peers. Once these skills are understood, the student should demonstrate a greater comfort in approaching peers, should better understand social reciprocity, and should have the ability to navigate a specific set of social norms. The teacher should be aware that how a student asks for help or solicits favors depends on the student's age and the cultural norms the student is raised in.

PHASE 1: Identifying what "help" and "favor" mean. Teach the student term specifics. Understanding the definition of "help" and the individual circumstances in which the student may require it is critical. This level of understanding is also necessary for the less concrete term "favor."

PHASE 2: Identifying whether help is needed or a favor desired. This distinction can be taught through use of discrimination teaching. The student should learn to identify situations where help is required versus those in which no help is needed, and situations where a favor is desired versus those the student can manage without assistance. This can be taught in several ways, including via the following methods:

- Write situations on recipe cards and read them to the student. The student should discriminate whether the situation requires asking for help or not, or asking for a favor or not.
- Set up situations in which the student may or may not require help, randomly occurring throughout the day. As the situation unfolds, the teacher should ask if the student needs help or a favor.
- Put the student in situations where help is required and wait for the student to identify the need for help (see "Communication Temptations" in *A Work in Progress*).

These situations should be systematically presented. Initially, they may be obvious to the student; in other words, the student should be able to discern whether help is needed rather easily. Over time, however, programming should move to less obvious and structured methods and less prompting—flash/recipe card discrimination being more artificial than "temptation" situations—and the situations should become more natural, less obvious, and more unpredictable. As the student demonstrates proficiency, the situations should change so that the need for help or a favor is more subtle as well. Consider the following examples:

Situations Clearly Requiring Assistance/Help/Favor

- The student is lost
- The student needs to get something beyond his or her reach
- The student cannot lift something needing to be moved

Less Obvious Situations

- The student wants a candy bar but doesn't have quite enough money
- The student wants to finish chores quickly so that he or she can watch a favorite television show
- The student is going on a vacation and needs someone to look after a pet

Over time and in a general sense, this skill should be generalized to situations naturally occurring throughout the student's day.

PHASE 3a: Identifying who can help. After successfully identifying whether help or a favor is required, the student should learn who is best to ask. Teaching the student to identify whether a person is a suitable "helper" will depend on the help or favor needed and the people available.

The following factors may make a person a good helping candidate:

- The person is able to help or do the favor
- The person is likely to help or do a favor
- The person may owe help or a favor (see the discussion of favor reciprocity later in this program)

Identification of potential sources of help is typically taught through discrimination training: The student must determine whether a candidate is good versus not good for a specific type of help. For example, if the student needs to reach something high, would a tall or short person be a good candidate? If the student is lost, would a police officer be a good candidate to help?

As the student develops proficiency in identifying whether someone would or would not be able to help, the teacher should help identify who would be the best candidate. For example, while away on vacation, the student needs someone to care for a pet hamster. Who would be a better candidate: a friend who likes animals or one who doesn't? Another consideration may be whether the student recently helped someone else. That person may be a better candidate than a friend who hasn't recently received a favor; people will be more likely to return a favor to someone who has helped them recently (favor reciprocity).

PHASE 3b: Getting more information about possible candidates. Prior to asking, the student can learn whether help is likely to be forthcoming and can be taught to more accurately assess this likelihood. To continue a previous example, if the student wants to know whether a friend will feed his hamster while he is away, he may ask informational questions such as "Do you like animals?" or "Are you in town next week?" If the responses are affirmative, he may proceed by asking for a favor. In contrast, if the answers are negative, the student should move on and assess another candidate.

This skill can be taught in a similar manner to Phase 3a, but in this case the student learns to generate the questions determining both whether someone is a helping candidate and what the likelihood that person will actually help is. In addition, the student learns to identify which responses would define a good candidate.

PHASE 4: Learning how to ask for help or a favor. After identifying who to ask, the student needs to learn how to ask for help or a favor. Typically, the student should first state what the problem is—why help is needed—and then request help. The student should be taught that "help" and "favor" requests need to be polite and presented as questions rather than demands. This phase can be taught using Teaching Interactions, with the request (the skill to be learned) having three basic components:

- State the problem.
- Ask for the help or favor.
- Be polite and present the request as a question.

Examples of "State the problem" might be:

- "My family is going to Florida next week and I need someone to feed the hamster."
- "I can't find the marbles."
- "My iPod ran out of battery power."
- "I'm hungry but don't have my wallet."

Corresponding examples of "Ask for the help or favor" combined with "Be polite and present the request as a question" are follows:

- "Would you be available to feed him for me?"
- "Can you help me look?"
- "Can I borrow yours for a while?"
- "Can I borrow some money for a sandwich?"

A possible skill addition may be to ask a setup question, such as "Can I ask you a favor?" or "Can you help me?" This would occur prior to the three steps described previously.

PHASE 5: Identifying when to ask. After mastering the issues of who and how to ask for help, the student should discriminate whether the time is right to do so. Favors and assistance are sometimes denied based on poor timing, rather than because the potential helper is not a good candidate or the request wasn't made appropriately. This skill may have been taught previously in social initiation programs; however, it becomes specifically relevant when asking for help or a favor. The student needs to catch the potential helper at a good time. Three factors must be considered:

- The timing is good for the student.
- The timing is good for the helping candidate.
- The timing is good for the act of helping.

For the initial consideration, the student should learn to ask for help before the situation becomes frustrating or stressful. For some students, this may mean learning to ask as soon as they know they need assistance. For others, self-monitoring may be required to determine individual stress/frustration thresholds. If the student demonstrates a grasp of self-monitoring and self-awareness, he or she may be taught to ask for help—depending on the situation—over a range of timing possibilities. Regardless, the student should learn to make requests at a time most suitable for the help requirements, without progressing beyond a mildly agitated state.

Frustration tolerance† or stress management† programs may be prerequisites to appropriately address this initial consideration. If the student is reluctant to ask for help at the early stages of agitation, Teaching Interactions may be required to help the student develop the ability to ask for help before agitation increases.

The second consideration requires the student to assess timing as it pertains to the potential helper. The candidate should be available (i.e., is not busy, occupied doing something else, and so on) and is in an agreeable mood. Have the student discriminate good versus bad timing when assessing the candidate's mood. The student can learn from illustrative pictures or from written/spoken scenarios. Teaching materials should clearly show the helping candidate represented in both good and bad timing situations. The teacher should guide the student in deciding whether he or she would or would not ask at that pictured/described moment.

Other timing considerations pertain to teaching such matters as asking for help sufficiently prior to when it needs to occur so that proper planning or preparation can take place.

†*Refer to A Work in Progress.*

PHASE 6: The student learns to appropriately respond to both accepted and denied help requests. In this phase, the student learns to graciously respond after either getting or not getting help or a favor. This behavior is important to establishing a respectful and polite manner of interacting.

If the potential helper cannot provide a favor or help, the student needs to follow several steps:

- Remain calm.
- Respond in some way, such as "Oh, okay," "Thanks anyway," or "Alright, no big deal."
- Begin the process of finding someone else suitable to provide assistance.

If the person agrees to help, the student should follow these steps:

- Thank the person.
- Follow through on the request (e.g., receive the borrowed iPod, take the money offered, give details about the hamster).
- Be prepared to do a favor or provide help to that person in the future.

Apologizing

Objectives

- Increased ability to maintain social interactions and friendships
- Increased understanding of social reciprocity
- Increased social awareness
- Increased understanding of feelings and emotions
- Enhanced expression of sincere emotions

Prerequisites

- Basic awareness of others★
- Cause and effect (especially pertaining to emotions)★
- Advanced phases require competencies in perspective taking and empathy

★See *A Work in Progress.*

Procedure

This program focuses on teaching students to apologize. The exact method of apologizing employed may differ slightly based on the age of the student and the culture in which the student lives.

PHASE 1: Facilitated apologizing—following the direction to apologize/compliance.
The goal of this phase is to teach the student to apologize in situations facilitated by an adult. Essentially, this phase is intended simply to prevent "further damage" from a peer's standpoint (and to address the needs of another child) after the student has done something wrong. The student is taught to follow an instruction that will require him or her to apologize to someone. For some students, this behavior may simply require them to learn what the instruction means and how to phrase an apology; for other students, it may also mean learning to comply with a nonpreferred instruction.

At this stage, the student is merely being asked to demonstrate a socially acceptable skill in situations where he or she may have wronged someone in an attempt to lessen the damage or stigma that may result from the student's previous actions. This skill, in essence, represents directed and rather rote responding, with a very specific and practical purpose. At this phase, the student is not expected to understand the need for an apology or the meaning of his or her actions.

The student can be taught to say a simple phrase: "I'm sorry that I . . . ," where the phrase ends with the student saying briefly what he or she did (and is apologizing for). Keep in mind that the student may find it easier to apologize for some situations than for others. It may be necessary to create a hierarchy so that the student can practice apologizing in situations that are easier (e.g., where student does not harbor ill will toward the person receiving the apology) prior to moving to more difficult situations.

It is imperative that the student's first exposure to apologizing in this program have positive consequences—for example, the apology is accepted and the student is able to resume reinforcing activity, or the apology is accepted and the "victim" shares a treat with the student. This relationship will attach a more positive connotation to apologizing than may already be present: For many students, being told to apologize often follows or is paired with negative consequences for the wrongdoing. If required, complying with being told to apologize can be paired with established reinforcement. However, be aware that the payoff for apologizing should not be so high as to make the initial wrongdoing a desirable behavior! Reinforcement should always be higher for not engaging in the original problem behavior and for seeking out appropriate alternatives.

For most children, it will be important to remain at this phase for a brief period, as the responding is essentially rote and dependent on adult initiation. To avoid dependency and a child getting "stuck" in rote responding, work on Phase 2 (and movement to additional phases) can occur simultaneously with (or at the least immediately following) effort on Phase 1.

PHASE 2a: Identifying the need to apologize. Recognition of the need to apologize can be taught as a discrimination program during which students identify situations in which an apology is required versus situations where an apology is not required. The following strategies may be considered during this phase:

- Writing situations on index cards, reading them to the student, and having the student identify if that is a situation where he or she should make an apology
- Presenting similar situations in videos or stories
- Having the student identify real-life situations where his or her feelings or someone else's feelings have been hurt or where the student has been upset or offended by the actions of another

Initially, these situations may be ones in which it is obvious to the student that he or she should apologize. As the student demonstrates proficiency, however, the situations would change so that the need for an apology becomes less obvious. Consider the following examples:

Situations Where an Apology Is Clearly Warranted

- Someone purposely uses aggression against another person
- Someone ruins someone else's property
- Someone says mean things to another person
- Someone purposely overturns a game while others are playing it

Situations Where an Apology Is Not Obviously Indicated, But Is Still Required

- Someone hurts someone by accident (bumps into the person)
- Someone's involuntary behavior affects another in a negative way (someone coughs throughout another person's presentation, causing distraction)
- Someone says something unkind to a third party about a person who isn't present, but the person finds out about the remark

- Someone mistakenly shares someone else's secret or news
- Someone accidentally trips over another person's block structure

Emphasize that when a person apologizes, he or she indicates regret for the decision made (even if the consequences were unforeseen) and notes that, given another opportunity, he or she would likely make a different decision.

PHASE 2b: Identifying the need to share "regrets." This advanced phase will not be suitable for all children.

Instead of making an apology, sometimes we simply express regret for events that occurred beyond our control or where the actions we took were taken for good reasons, and would likely be taken again in the future. In these cases, we do not regret the occurrence or the decision we made, but we do regret the consequences that the incident had for others. In some of these cases, good social skills call for a person to express "regrets" and even to say he or she is "sorry."

Examples of situations where expressing regret demonstrates good social skills (but an apology is not required) include the following circumstances:

- Someone is sick and cannot make a play date
- Someone cannot attend a party of a friend because he or she has a previous commitment
- Someone cannot do a favor for a friend because the person will be out of town

PHASE 3: How to apologize. After identifying that an apology is required, the student needs to learn the steps to independently apologize. Depending on the level of the student, demonstration of proficiency in one, several, or all of the following steps may be appropriate. Step 3 will require the student's understanding of perspective taking and progress in showing true empathy and concern, so it may not be appropriate for all students. Also, the student must be taught that the apology should be delivered in a polite tone of voice and that establishing eye contact when delivering the apology is preferable.

Teaching the following steps may be done by using Teaching Interactions. As always, age-appropriate language and cultural norms must be considered before choosing how best to teach the student.

1. State the wrongdoing and say you are sorry. For example:

- I'm sorry I drew on your picture.
- Sorry I knocked over your drink.
- Sorry I told Jesse that you were breaking up with him.

2. Provide an explanation (unless it is obvious or there is no excuse—discrimination training may be necessary here). For example:

- I was mad that yours was better than mine.
- I didn't see you there.
- I thought you had already told him.

3. State concern for the person's feelings. For example:

- I bet you were really mad that your picture was ruined.
- I hope it doesn't stain your shirt.
- I bet that made it really hard for you.

4. Assure and/or make (if possible) amends (this step not necessary with "regrets"). For example:

- I won't do it again.
- I need to look where I'm going.
- I'll mind my own business in the future.

PHASE 4: Identifying the presentation, form, and type of apology required. After the student has identified that he or she needs to apologize and knows how to deliver an apology, the student needs to be taught to choose the best manner and circumstances to apologize. Teaching the student to identify the best time and place and method (verbal or written) and type of apology (full apology or regret) will depend on the wrongdoing and the person to whom the student is apologizing.

Step 1: Decide whether to make a verbal or written apology

Verbal apologies tend to be used in situations where the student is very familiar with the person to whom he or she is apologizing. Written apologies tend to be used in more formal situations (such as community-related wrongdoings) or with people with whom the student may be less familiar. Again, a discrimination program may be set up where the student decides the best type of apology to make.

The following factors may make a verbal or written apology more appropriate:

- The person is a close friend or family member (verbal)
- The person is someone the student knows in a formal capacity, such as the manager of a store in which an incident happened or the principal of his or her school– (written)
- The student will see the person before he or she has time to write a letter (verbal)
- The student struggles with anxiety in confrontational situations (written)

Step 2: Identify when to apologize

After identifying how he or she will apologize, the student needs to determine when is the best time to apologize or when is *not* a good time. This skill may have been taught previously in social initiation programs, but its importance increases when apologizing is involved.

The following factors should be considered in this step:

- Whether it is a good time for the student to apologize
- Whether it is a good time for the person he or she is apologizing to

- What the level of the transgression was (more serious wrongdoings require more immediate action)
- How much time it may take for making amends
- What the student's relationship with the aggrieved party is

In regards to the first factor, the student shouldbe as relaxed as possible and no longer have feelings of frustration associated with the event when making an apology. For some students, time to "cool off" may be needed before the student attempts to apologize. For other students, self-monitoring on their own behalf as to their level of stress may be required, so that they can ensure they are able to make a polite apology and remain in control even if the apology is not accepted.

The second consideration focuses on the need to approach the person at a time when the candidate is available and is not overly frustrated or upset. Teaching this skill may involve having the student do a discrimination during which he or she has to identify a good time versus a bad time to apologize with regard to the person's mood and emotional level. For example, the teacher might show pictures or relate scenarios that involve a person being in situations that would be good times to apologize versus bad times to apologize; the student would be asked to decide whether he or she would or would not apologize at that moment. Examples of bad times might include the following scenarios:

- The person is clearly upset (crying, yelling, cursing)
- The person is clearly busy
- The person is with other people with whom he or she may not want to share the event (especially if it causes some embarrassment)
- Interrupting the person (i.e., at work) would not be appropriate

PHASE 5: Responding to the person depending on whether the apology was accepted.
Some students may need to be taught to discriminate which responses mean that a person has accepted versus not accepted the apology. This can be done through a discrimination program. Emphasize that the student should attend to facial expression, tone of voice, and the person's actual words to help identify whether the apology has been accepted. Role-plays are an excellent way to teach this skill.

As soon as the student knows whether the apology has been accepted, he or she needs to respond appropriately, especially when the person to whom he has apologized does not accept the apology. The student can be taught the following steps through Teaching Interactions:

- Remain calm.
- Respond in some way indicating understanding (e.g., "Oh, okay"; "Thanks for your time").
- Leave the situation.

Programs such as those dealing with stress management and frustration tolerance may be required to help students remain calm in these situations.

If the person accepts the apology, the student needs to recognize that further steps are required:

- Thank the person.
- Do his or her best to truly make amends (e.g., do not repeat the wrongdoing).
- Be prepared to accept to reciprocate by accepting an apology from that person in the future.

Arguing, Discussing, Persuading, and Letting Go

Objectives

- Develop a better understanding of the difference between arguing and discussing
- Determine when to maintain and when to stop an argument or discussion
- Learn to speak with—and not at—others
- Increase peer comfort levels
- Develop tools to change others' opinions

Prerequisites

- Topical conversation skills★
- Reading others' verbal and nonverbal responses to one's behavior
- Responding to others' verbal and nonverbal responses to one's behavior
- Perspective taking

★See *A Work in Progress.*

Procedure

Teaching Interactions are used for the following phases. Included within the Teaching Interaction format are role-plays and movement to naturally occurring situations (generalization training). Discrimination training, using a Discrete Trial Teaching format, is of particular importance to this skill area. The skills covered in this section are most relevant for persons aged 7 through adult.

PHASE 1: Discrimination training in a series of areas. Initially, the student learns to identify the difference between argumentation and discussion. Then, the student learns to identify those situations when arguments (e.g., the student standing up for himself or herself) or discussions (e.g., someone having incorrect information, authority figures are involved) would be most appropriate. Next, discrimination sessions focus on issues and situations significant to continuing a discussion or argument, and circumstances when letting go makes the most sense. Finally, the student participates in discrimination work on situations in which others are, and are not, successfully persuaded.

PHASE 2: Constructive discussions. The elements of constructive discussions are taught and practiced:

- Calm manner and voice tone
- Listening to and recalling what others are saying
- Being open to the other side

- Not interrupting
- Responding to or rebutting the other's points briefly and politely
- Stating your own points briefly and clearly
- Avoiding repeating and "round and round" arguments
- Finding areas of agreement
- Accepting areas of disagreement

PHASE 3: Constructive argumentation. The components of constructive argumentation are taught and practiced:

- Using a raised voice tone (without yelling and aggression)
- Using voice and gestures for emphasis
- Listening to what others are saying
- Trying to understand the other side
- Rebutting what others are saying without denigration
- Stating one's own points briefly and clearly
- Using personal feelings statements as appropriate
- Maintaining calm
- Avoiding tangents
- Avoiding interruptions
- Refraining from personal attacks
- Asserting oneself clearly if not allowed to speak or attacked
- Ending the engagement if hostility is increasing
- Ending the engagement if there is no progress
- Ending the engagement if there is compromise or agreement

PHASE 4: Artful persuasion. The elements of artful persuasion are taught and practiced:

- Evaluating the other person's needs, feelings, and beliefs regarding a theme, activity, item, or issue
- Listening to and expressing understanding regarding the other person's thoughts, feelings, and position on the topic
- Providing clear rationales that are meaningful to the other person
- Providing strong examples that are meaningful to the other person
- Answering questions honestly and supportively
- Using pace and momentum
- Building on areas of acceptance and agreement
- Allowing space and time for reflection
- Avoiding redundancy, pressure, and bullying
- Ending on a note of progress
- Ending when there is no progress
- Ending when someone is convinced

PHASE 5: Generalization. The student is systematically taught to apply skills from role-play scenarios to orchestrated arrangements and, ultimately, to naturally occurring situations.

Go with the Flow (Flow of Conversation)

Objectives

- Develop understanding of the elements of group conversation
- Develop understanding and awareness of an aspect of the group social process
- Enhance social conversational skills
- Increase acceptance by peers
- Enhance the ability to lead and follow in a group

Prerequisites

- Conversational topics★
- Commenting★
- Question asking★

★See *A Work in Progress.*

Procedure

Teaching Interactions are used for the various phases. Included as part of the Teaching Interaction format are discrimination trainings, role-plays, and movement to naturally occurring situations. The skills covered in this program are most relevant for persons aged 8 to 13.

PHASE 1: Discrimination training—Part 1. While observing samples of conversation (videotaped samples may be easiest to utilize), the student learns to identify and discriminate between active/continuous conversation and pauses in conversation. The student should indicate (e.g., call out, raise a hand, thumb up versus thumb down) when the conversation is active and when a pause has occurred.

PHASE 2: Discrimination training—Part 2. While observing videotaped samples of conversation, the student learns to identify and discriminate between the speeding up of conversation flow, the winding down of conversation flow, and the discontinuation of the topic. The student should indicate each of these conditions to demonstrate understanding of this aspect of conversation.

PHASE 3: Discrimination training—Part 3: In vivo. The student is presented with conversations in vivo and must identify when there is active conversation flow, acceleration and deceleration of the conversation flow, and pausing or discontinuation of the topics.

PHASE 4: Conversational flow. In this phase, the student is taught to recognize and use methods for maintaining conversational flow.

- Reflective and relevant commenting:
  - "No way!"
  - "You cannot be serious!"
  - "Tell me more."
- Questions for elaboration:
  - "And then what happened?"
- Questions for clarification:
  - "Who is she?"
- Praise and compliments:
  - "Dude, that is so cool!"
- Relating the topic to oneself:
  - "I saw that, too!"
- Opening new, but related, areas of discussion:
  - "That's like when my little brother . . ."

PHASE 5: When to apply methods. In this phase, the student learns to reduce the frequency with which the previously described methods are used when conversation flow is accelerating and to increase their use when the pace is slowing down.

PHASE 6: Transitions. In this phase, the student learns methods for transitioning to new topics and restarting conversational flow when the conversation has halted.

- Making a process comment:
  - "Seems that's all talked out."
- Asking a discussion-opening question:
  - "Did you see the game last night?"
- Making a discussion-opening, reflective comment:
  - "I heard *Borat* was so gross."
- Returning to an earlier conversation:
  - "When we talked about your dad's car before, I forgot to ask you . . ."

The student is also taught to discriminate when another person is attempting to renew conversational flow and when an absence of conversation appears to be preferred by the group (e.g., when attempts to restart conversation do not catch on) and to terminate restart efforts.

PHASE 7: The student is systematically taught to use skills by moving from role-play, to in vivo practice, and ultimately to naturally occurring situations.

SOCIAL
INTERACTION

Responsiveness

Objectives

- Teach the student to attend and respond to the initiations of others
- Increase environmental and social awareness
- Facilitate social interaction
- Increase acceptance by peers

Procedure

The core objective of this program is for the student to respond to both verbal and nonverbal initiations of others (e.g., statements, questions, directives, gestures) in naturally occurring situations. Ultimately, these initiations should occur when the student is not expecting them.

Given the nature of this skill, the target is "first-time responding" to a social initiation. Therefore, immediately repeated practice following an initial trial (correct or incorrect) will be irrelevant to the learning of this skill. That is, the second trial is never an opportunity for "first-time responding." Strategically spacing the learning trials is important. Doing so will afford the student sufficient opportunities to learn the skill, while leaving adequate time between trials to establish the appropriate stimulus conditions (i.e., another "first time") for the response. This practice also helps avoid undesired prompting (providing repeated chances).

It is also recommended that, in work in this area, within-stimulus prompting—rather than external prompting—is utilized. For example, rather than a second instruction to respond from a therapist after the student fails to respond to the greeting of another (which would also be a problem "second chance" trial as noted previously), on the next "first chance" trial the initiator would greet the student with greater emphasis (e.g., more loudly, after receiving eye contact, in closer proximity). This within-stimulus or emphasis prompt would then be faded across "first chance" trials. Priming-type prompts (i.e., reminders before initiations) would be preferred to external prompts, but may be less effective than within-stimulus prompting strategies.

Initially, the student should practice the skill during periods when the likelihood of responding will be the greatest. Responses can be both verbal and nonverbal, as appropriate (e.g., gestures, acknowledgment, orienting toward the speaker, eye contact, comments, answering the question, following the requested action). Teach the student to respond in a natural, age-appropriate manner. Situations may need to be created to allow sufficient opportunities (over a period of time) to practice skills so that generalized learning can occur.

PHASE 1: In structured teaching situations, teach the student to orient to the initiations of others while engaged in a neutral, independent activity. Orientation may include glancing, looking toward, and turning toward others. The response should be shaped to have a *natural duration*. While this skill is a critical component of social responsivity, it should be expanded upon as quickly as possible. Examples of appropriate orientation include the following responses:

- The student looks up at the speaker.
- The student turns around and looks toward a person who has just tapped his or her back.
- The student turns toward someone who has just called his or her name.

PHASE 2: In structured situations, teach the student to respond appropriately to the other's attempted initiations—either nonverbally or verbally—while engaged in a neutral independent activity. The student should also be expected to incorporate the orienting response learned in Phase 1. Examples of appropriate responding include the following:

- Someone walks into the room and says "Hi" to the student; the student looks up and waves at the person.
- Mom asks, "Do you want a cookie?" The student looks up and says, "Yes,"

Phases 3 through 9 teach the student to consistently engage in appropriate responsive behavior with increasingly natural circumstances and levels of distraction. These phases can be taught simultaneously, with the teacher selecting those variables that are most functional, meaningful, and achievable. The student may already be proficient with some variables, so these can be skipped. That being said, objectively assessing these skills regularly—ensuring that they are demonstrated in a wide variety of naturally occurring situations—is critical.

PHASE 3: The student learns to respond to increasingly less direct initiations. Use of the student's name at the beginning of the initiation is an effective way to ensure attention. However, this prompt should be faded as soon as possible to more naturally occurring instances.

Type of Initiation
• Using the student's name
• Question directed to the student
• General comment

PHASE 4: The student learns to respond while engaged in increasingly more preferred activities (i.e., those from which the student is not easily distracted or not readily discontinued).

Preference of Activity
• Neutral activity
• Preferred activity
• Highly preferred activity

PHASE 5: The student learns to respond while engaged in increasingly less structured activities.

Degree of Structure
• Structured activity
• Structured play
• Free play

PHASE 6: The student learns to respond when engaged in activities with increasing numbers of people.

Size of Group
• One-on-one
• Small group
• Large group

PHASE 7: The student learns to respond to people who are increasingly less familiar and authoritative.

Person
• Therapist/parent
• Familiar peers
• Less familiar but known peers

PHASE 8: The student learns to respond to people initiating from an increased distance.

Proximity
• Next to the student
• Within the area
• Outside the area

PHASE 9: The student learns to respond to others in increasingly natural settings.

Location
• Clinic/home
• School
• Community

Initiating Social Contact and Interaction

Objectives

- Teach the student to independently socialize with peers and others
- Increase environmental and social awareness
- Facilitate positive social interaction and social play
- Increase responsiveness and acceptance by peers

Prerequisites

- Social tolerance
- Basic environmental and social awareness★
- Basic responsiveness to others' initiations
- Basic expressive ability★
- Social motivation
- Joint attending

★See *A Work in Progress.*

Procedure

This program's ultimate goal is for the student to *independently* initiate social contact and interchanges. The focus should be expressly on increasing greater independent behavior within naturally occurring social situations. In this light, staff-directed initiations (e.g., "Go ask Bobby if he needs help") may teach instruction following, but provide limited—if any—learning of independent initiation. A strategy that involves external prompts (e.g., instructions, pointing, reminders, leading questions) may produce performance but tends to interfere with development of *independent* and *spontaneous* initiations.

A minimally intrusive and easier-to-fade strategy for this critical skill may be "within-stimulus" prompting. These prompts tend to highlight facets of antecedent stimuli, typically through exaggeration or emphasis. An example of this type of prompt may be found in the following scenario: When teaching a student to approach a specific peer, initially the peer's proximity may be very close to the student, with the peer prominently engaged in a compelling activity, making the social initiation more inevitable. Over time, these features are faded to represent more natural environmental antecedent situations for initiation.

For this program, fitting, thoughtful prompting strategies and teaching techniques are used in conjunction with reinforcement systems (as appropriate to the individual student) to encourage greater independent social initiation. Further, use of motivating operations (similar to the "Communication Temptations" program in *A Work in Progress*)—that is, utilizing "social-initiation temptations"— would be the instructional approach of choice. This goes against typical social programming. Why?

Although it is customary for social-initiation programming to begin with greetings, we would argue against such an approach. Greetings tend to not result in any meaningful intrinsic or natural reinforcement. This would be akin to beginning an independent communication-initiation program with commenting. Therefore, social-initiation programming should most typically begin with social-initiation temptation-type work. In such a manner, not only are specific initiations developed, but so is the student's social intent and sense of the power of social approach (much the same as how the power of language and communicative intent is facilitated by "communication temptations").

For all phases, prompting dimensions—such as peer proximity, setting context, activity involved, and number of peers present—should be systematically faded to approximate more naturally occurring conditions.

PHASE 1: Initiation temptations. Contrived situations are created that serve as "social-initiation temptations" for the student. Depending on what is reinforcing to the student and his or her requisite skills, these scenarios may include the following skills:

- Requesting (verbally or nonverbally) an item, activity, or action (e.g., something preferred, something necessary to a task or activity) from a peer
- Asking a peer for assistance or help (e.g., to complete a preferred activity, to get a want satisfied)
- Asking (needed) information-seeking questions (to complete an assignment or get a preferred object or activity)
- Verbally or gesturally requesting attention, response, or approval (e.g., using a peer's name, saying "Look") from a peer

Be sure to fade the artificiality of the "initiation temptation" as the student progresses so as to mimic more naturally occurring situations.

PHASE 2: Play/activity initiations are practiced and taught. Rather than teaching the student the request, "Can I play?" (which is rarely used by typically developing peers, is often a setup for rejection, and is too formal and adult-like for most age groups), a more natural social/play initiation sequence is taught, paired with reinforcement (as appropriate to the individual student). Pairing up the skill sequence with reinforcement increases the likelihood the student will be motivated to use it. However, as with other types of impediments to more independent functioning, the reinforcement schedule should be faded as practically and quickly as possible. A task-analyzed example follows:

- The student walks over to where the peer is playing.
- The student stands near where the peer is playing (approximately 3 to 5 feet away—not too close to appear odd, not so far away as to miss what's going on) and watches play for a brief period (15 to 20 seconds, depending on the activity).

- The student assesses if the peer is comfortable or uncomfortable with the approach.
  - If the peer appears uncomfortable, the student should leave.
  - If the peer appears comfortable, the student should make an appropriate comment (something related to what is occurring in the play situation, such as "I have one of those") or ask a relevant question ("Is that new?").
- The student assesses the peer's response to the verbal approach.
  - If the peer ignores or responds in an annoyed or unfriendly manner, the student should leave.
  - If peer responds positively or asks the student to join, student should do so
  - If the peer responds in a friendly manner, the student then asks a "join-in" question (e.g., "Can I try that?" or "Can I see?"), makes a "joining-in" comment (e.g., "I know how to work that" or "I have one of those at home!"), or gradually moves toward joining in the activity.
  - If the peer objects, refuses, or says, "No," the student should make a good-bye statement (e.g., "Okay," "Maybe another time") and leave.
  - If the peer starts interactive play, responds affirmatively, or says, "Sure" or "Yes," the student should join in.

Other play initiations may include the following scenarios:

- Inviting a peer into an ongoing activity/play
- Choosing a partner
- Picking members for a team (selecting teammates)
- Asking a peer for a play date
- Choosing an activity that is likely to entice peers to join in

PHASE 3: Social greetings. Although greetings and introductions are often considered social skills of primary importance, in many cases they are not behaviors that young, typically developing children engage in with peers with great frequency. Exceptions exist, of course, such as situations requiring more formal greetings, seeing someone not seen in a long time, or close peers offering each other hugs. Therefore, once initiations consistently result in meaningful social reinforcement is consistently occurring, work on greetings can begin as indicated.

It's worth repeating: External, verbal or adult prompting (e.g., "Say 'Hi'," "What should you say?" pointing,) should be kept to a minimum. These prompts are difficult to fade, and their use is contradictory to the development of independence and spontaneity. Within-stimulus prompts (e.g., having the peer initially enter a room in dramatic fashion with an eager, expectant expression on his or her face), gradually faded to more typical antecedents, are best when teaching independent, first-time greeting. Reinforcement is utilized in conjunction with prompting and prompt fading. Effort should be directed at ensuring greetings are natural, relaxed, age appropriate, culturally fitting, and typical (including facial expression, gaze, verbal content, voice tone, affect, and the extent to which they are offhanded and fleeting—based on age and cultural appropriateness).

PHASE 4: Other communication initiations. Remarks, comments, and statements sometimes made in offhanded fashion may be used as conversation and interaction starters. Strategic use of Teaching Interactions in conjunction with (as with greetings) within-stimulus prompts and differential reinforcement as necessary is recommended. Also as with greetings, shaping to naturalistic style is essential.

PHASE 5: Advanced, higher-order initiations. With gains in the consistency of initiations contained in the preceding phases, social initiations in behalf or in the interest of peers should be taught. Such work begins with discrimination training designed to help the child identify situations in which he or she should engage in initiation, prior to his or her involvement being requested by another. Teaching interactions and reinforcement, faded to natural situations and outcomes, are applied to teach such skills as the following:

- Providing help and assistance
- Offering caring and comfort
- Interacting with someone who seems lonely or bored
- Offering congratulations (see the "Giving Compliments" program)
- Standing up for a friend

Play: Reciprocity and Flow

Objectives

- Increased ability to listen to peers' ideas
- Increased initiation of play ideas
- Enhanced quality of interactions with others
- Increased understanding of reciprocity in play
- Increased flexibility in play

Prerequisites

- Receptive instructions★
- Nonverbal imitation★
- Giving instructions

★See *A Work in Progress.*

Procedure

This program teaches students to accept suggestions other children make during play and, in later phases, to make suggestions to other students as a means to promote reciprocity and continue the flow of play. Initially, the material should be approached in a systematic, structured manner, teaching the student the basics of accepting or making an offer. As the student's proficiency increases, the teaching should become less structured and more naturalistic.

PHASE 1: "Yes, let's!": Accepting offers. Pick an activity the student enjoys. For some students, this can involve actual object or toy play and then move to imaginative activities. Other students may begin immediately with less structured imaginative play.

The teacher makes a suggestion about what to do. Have the student respond by verbally agreeing to the activity and then following through by participating with the teacher. Initially, suggestions should be simple, quickly performed activities. After the child has agreed to and participated in the first activity, the teacher makes another suggestion, still focused around the activity. The teacher should make multiple suggestions in a short period of time so momentum is established and the student practices the skill repeatedly over a short period of time. Consider the following examples:

- The student and the teacher both have superhero figures.
  - Teacher: "Let's fly to Mars!"
  - Student: "Yes, let's!" (The teacher flies his figure into the bathroom; the student follows/imitates)
  - Teacher: "Let's get stuck under the waterfall!"

162

- Student: "Yes, let's!" (The teacher turns on the tap, and both teacher and student put their figures under the running water)
- Teacher: "Aliens are invading! Ack! Slimed!"
- Student: "Slimed!" (The teacher squirts liquid soap on his figure; the student imitates)
- Teacher: "Let's escape the aliens and fly to safety!"
- Student: "Yes, let's!" (The teacher flies his figure out of bathroom and the student follows)

- The student and the teacher both have a piece of paper.
  - Teacher: "Let's draw a circle."
  - Student: "Yes, okay!" (The teacher and the student each draw a circle)
  - Teacher: "Let's draw square eyes in the circle."
  - Student: "Yes, okay!" (The teacher and the student each draw square eyes in the circle)
  - Teacher: "Let's draw eight arms coming out of our circle."
  - Student: "Yes, okay!" (The teacher and the student each draw eight arms coming out of the circle)
  - Teacher: "Let's color our robots gray and black."
  - Student: "Yes, okay!"

- The student and teacher are sitting on chairs in the playroom.
  - Teacher: "Let's climb this mountain!"
  - Student: "Yes, cool!" (The teacher mimes climbing a mountain; the student imitates)
  - Teacher: "Let's get to the top and have a picnic."
  - Student: "Yes, cool!" (The teacher mimes taking out picnic basket; the student imitates)
  - Teacher: "Let's drink all our chocolate milk first!"
  - Student: "Yes, let's!" (The teacher mimes drinking milk; the student imitates)
  - Teacher: "Let's burp really loud!"
  - Student, "Okay!" (The teacher makes a loud burping noise; the student imitates)

As the student demonstrates proficiency, responds verbally, and follows the action (whether by imitating the teacher's model or simply by following the teacher's suggestion) with less prompts, the activity can become more natural:

- Vary the language the student uses to accept the offer (e.g., "Yes, let's!" "Okay!" "Cool!" "Good idea!").
- Add sound effects to play scenarios and encourage imitation.
- Increase the time spent actually doing the action suggested so there is more actual play going on.
- Increase the complexity of suggestions.
- Increase the specificity of suggestions.
- When the student has adequate receptive language to understand suggestions, provide differential reinforcement for following the suggestion without waiting to imitate the teacher.

PHASE 2: "Yes, let's!": Making offers. The student learns to make suggestions in play as a means to advance the play. The student should walk the line between offering suggestions in a participatory manner versus taking over the play situation. In addition to teaching the student about initiating suggestions, a sense of reciprocity in play is further developed.

The student has learned to expect multiple suggestions continuing the play scenario from Phase 1. In Phase 2, the student learns to initiate the suggestions and share the responsibility with the teacher.

As with Phase 1, the teacher begins the session by making a suggestion, and the student accepts and participates. For this phase, however, the teacher then waits (rather than continuing the suggestion chain). This wait period is the instruction/temptation for the student to make a suggestion. If the student does so, continue with the play scenario, switching back and forth with the play suggestions. If the student does not initiate a suggestion after the teacher waits, a delayed prompt is appropriate (gestural: shrug of the shoulders, expectant look on the face; verbal: "I need a new idea," "Well?").

Once the student makes a suggestion (prompted or independent), the teacher should respond excitedly ("Yes, let's!") and continue the scenario. Consider the following example:

- Teacher: "Let's be pirates and get in our ship."
- Student: "Yes, let's!" (The student and the teacher climb on a couch and stand on it)
- Teacher: "Ahhhh! Water on deck! We're sinking!"
- Student: "Yeah!" (The student and teacher look down at their feet)
- The teacher waits, and looks at the student. If the student doesn't make a suggestion, the teacher shrugs his shoulders.
- Student: "Let's jump out of our boat!" (Prompted trial)
- Teacher: "Great idea!" (The teacher and the student jump off the couch)
- Teacher: "Look, there's land over there!" (The teacher points to a rug)
- Student: "Yes!" (The student points, too)
- Teacher: "Land ho!"
- The teacher waits, and looks at the student. (Reduced prompt)
- Student: "Let's swim to land!"
- Teacher: "Yes, let's!" (The student and the teacher mime swimming to land)

If the student requires assistance in generating suggestions, consider the following prompt ideas:

- Write suggestions related to the theme on index cards and have the student choose one.
- Talk about ideas for the play prior to beginning so the student has some references to pull from (priming).
- Read a book or watch a show on the play theme and discuss suggestions while doing so. This will help the student recall suggestions during the play scenario.
- Have props available relating to the theme so the student can generate suggestions from the props. For example, if you are playing cars, you might have tools on the floor to help the student generate an idea about cars breaking down.

- If the student continues to struggle with taking the initiative to direct play or make ongoing suggestions, a more intrusive prompt, if necessary, may be the following: A transition object—something passed between the play partners—can be utilized to signal the student taking control of the play. For example, if you are playing pirates, the captain's hat could symbolize who is responsible for making suggestions.

PHASE 3: Generalization to peers. Skill generalization may begin with the introduction of a peer or several peers. This step alone will likely cause some hiccups in the student's ability to perform the learned skills. With that possibility in mind, initially the skill may be couched in a more structured presentation. For example, the group can participate in a game of reciprocity. In the first round, a peer makes all the suggestions for play as well as the continuation phrases for ongoing play. Round two may consist of the student taking a turn doing the same. Over time, this reciprocity game can begin with the student and, eventually, the game's goal becomes taking turns guiding play. This structure can be faded as the student demonstrates a greater ability to generate suggestions, follow suggestions, and, most critically, transition between being the "suggestee" and the "suggester" fluently, as the play evolves and progresses.

PHASE 4: Reciprocal storytelling: Flexibility, creativity, and story participation. The teacher begins this skill development by telling a story aloud. The teacher can pretend to be a storyteller, or pretend to be typing the story as it is unfolding aloud. The student listens to the story and should be prepared to jump in and act out parts of the story when called on to do so. The level of language involved in the story and the level of participation required should be individualized, based on the student's receptive and expressive language abilities.

In addition, to encourage participation, the story's theme can initially be based on the student's interests. Over time, the themes should be as far ranging as is appropriate for the student's age and the culture of play the student's peers participate in. The student's actions should have a range as well, from reality-based with actual props and activities, to imagination or fantasy based, with pretend props and miming actions. To quickly establish the understanding necessary to participate in this activity, the story should initially be reality based with real props and real actions. Consider the following example:

- Teacher: "Once upon a time, there was a boy named (student's name)."
- The teacher prompts the student to stand up.
  - Prompt as unobtrusively as possible; this may be a pause paired with a look of expectation, a nod, and a motion to stand up. Try not use verbal prompts.
- "He was a champion dragon-slayer and had a really sharp sword."
  - A "sword" has already been put near the student; the student should pick it up and admire it. If necessary, prompts may include pointing to the sword, nodding toward, it, and so on. Again, avoid verbal prompts to get the response from the student.

- "The sword was light, yet powerful!"
  - The student swashbuckles, waving the "sword" expertly.
- Teacher: "One day, the dragon-slayer was running through the forest . . ."
- The student begins running around the room, pretending to be in the forest. Again, follow effective prompting strategies as necessary.
- ". . . when he saw a dragon!"
  - A stuffed dragon has already been placed on the floor somewhere.
- Teacher: "(Student) said, "Prepare to die, dragon!"
  - This is actually an instruction (verbal imitation) that the student should follow.
  - Student: "Prepare to die, dragon!"

As the student understands the expectations and becomes proficient in following the story, the teacher can extend the activity:

- Move from more reality-based scenarios to more imaginative scenarios.
  - Use objects to represent other objects.
  - Change the name of the main character from the student's name.
  - Have the student mime actions rather than use real props.
- Allow the student to make his or her own statements.
  - Teacher: "And the (student) said, . . ." The student fills in the dialogue.
- Allow the student to generate his or her own actions.
  - Teacher: "And then (student) . . ." The student fills the gap with an action compatible with the story.
- For students with more expressive language, the teacher and student can reverse roles so the student gets practice generating ideas and stories as well as watching the teacher and changing the story based on the teacher's actions.

PHASE 5: Reciprocal storytelling: Listening and interacting as a member of a group. This activity can be performed in a group, with multiple students playing different characters in the story. The benefit of this more natural presentation is the potential to increase the student's ability to listen and better attend to peers. As the student becomes more proficient, the teacher can reduce the amount of storytelling and allow the student and peers to more spontaneously and independently interact and maintain the play flow.

Who Do You Choose?
(Choosing Peers for Social
Interaction)

Objectives

- Develop the ability to make social judgments
- Develop authentic peer relationships
- Increase the likelihood of successful social interactions
- Develop decision-making and problem-solving skills
- Increase learning opportunities available from both peers and natural situations
- Increase self-awareness
- Develop critical thinking skills

Prerequisites

- "Ranking strategy" understanding and use
- Catagories★
- Receptive language★
- Expressive language★

★See *A Work in Progress.*

Procedure

Depending on the student's skill level and abilities, creating written or pictorial cards depicting peers, social qualities (for ranking), and specific activities may be helpful. Alternatively, a dry-erase board could be used to create rankings and quality lists specific to each activity being examined. Using these materials would bring a visual component to this program's beginning phases, possibly making the material more accessible.

Considering a comprehensive variety of desirable qualities related to each activity is critical. In later phases, self-monitoring strategies could assist in developing greater independence and sustained use of this skill.

PHASE 1: The student discriminates between desirable and undesirable personal qualities specific to activities. The student learns to identify personal qualities and features that are either desirable or undesirable when applied to specific activities. This discrimination will assist the student in better identifying peers to work or play with during those activities. The student should further explain how the desired qualities are related to success in the specific activity. The student should then rank the qualities—from most to least important—for each activity. The "quality" lists should be individualized to the student's own personal strengths and deficits and based on each activity. Thus the qualities in each list will differ for each student and possibly for each activity (although "quality" overlap between activities is certainly possible).

EXAMPLE 1: "Who would be best for you to sit next to in class?"

Good Qualities	Poor Qualities
Listens well	Shouts out
Follows classroom rules	Talks too much
Joins in discussions	Teases
Doesn't fidget	Is out of the seat a lot

EXAMPLE 2: "Who would be good to play games with at recess?"

Good Qualities	Poor Qualities
Someone with similar interests	Someone who causes trouble
Someone in the same grade	Someone known for cheating
A cooperative person	Someone who is overly controlling
Someone who enjoys games	Someone who can't focus
Someone involved	Someone much younger

EXAMPLE 3: "Who would you choose to be on your team?"

Good Qualities	Poor Qualities
Competitive	A slacker
Athletic	Clumsy
Someone who is good at the sport	Someone who isn't interested in the sport
A team player	Someone who "goes it alone"

EXAMPLE 4: "Who would you choose as a study partner?"

Good Qualities	Poor Qualities
Someone proficient at the subject	Someone with poor study habits
Someone who can explain well	Someone with attendance problems
Someone interested in the topic	A person who isn't in your class

PHASE 2: The student generates a list of possible peer choices. The list should include most available peers. For each activity, the student should identify the peers who have desirable qualities specific to that activity and the peers who lack those qualities. If possible, the student should rank-order the peers for the specific activity, taking into account the most relevant qualities for that activity.

Example: "Who is a good choice to sit next to in class?"

Good Peer Choices   **Poor Peer Choices**

(The student lists peers based on both the activity and the personal qualities deemed relevant to success in that activity.)

PHASE 3: Beginning to plan and participate in activities armed with relevant choices. The student plans to participate in the specific activity and selects the peers previously identified as "good" choices.

PHASE 4: Activity review. The student reviews the success of the plan with a teacher and determines if adjustments to the peer choices or the qualities used for selection need to be made.

PHASE 5: Transfer of the system. The student plans and participates in a gradually increasing number of activities occurring throughout the day. At this point, the student should choose different peers in the "good choices" column depending on the activities. This will reduce the likelihood the student will become repetitive when choosing peers. Further, it will increase the likelihood of successful interaction for the student across peers.

PHASE 6: Further generalization. The same process and system can be used to teach the student to make decisions regarding activity selection.

Example: "What should I play at recess?"

GOOD CHOICES	POOR CHOICES
Something lots of kids play[†]	Something few kids play[†]
Something my friends play	My friends don't play this game
Boys play it[†]	Girls play it[†]
Something I am good at	Something I don't know well

[†]*Taking into account age, gender, and grade culture.*

Being a Good Sport

Objectives

- Facilitate overall success in organized play/sport
- Increase interactional reciprocity
- Increase concern regarding the needs and interests of others

Prerequisites

- Conversation skills (intermediate)★
- Cause and effect (basic)★

★See *A Work in Progress.*

Procedure

Depending on the student's skill level and ability set, Discrete Trial Teaching or Teaching Interactions may be used for various elements of the skill instruction.

PHASE 1: Offering congratulations during noncompetitive moments. The student is taught to congratulate a peer when not an opponent of or in competition with that peer. This would most likely occur when the student is watching the peer play a game or a sport (as a spectator). See the "Giving Compliments" program.

PHASE 2: Cheering. Teach the student when cheering a peer is appropriate (e.g., when the peer has scored, is running to first base, is racing toward a touchdown, or has rolled a particularly good pair of dice during a board game). The student should learn the basic components required for cheering appropriately. The following component analysis can be used as a guide but should be individualized to the student. Prior discrimination training and specific skill instruction (e.g., work on positive statements or appropriate gestures) would occur as indicated.

- The student learns to shift his or her attention between the game/activity and the peer being cheered on.
  - The student learns to focus attention (e.g., physical orientation, eye gaze, listening) for meaningful periods of time between the activity/game and the peer (approximately 5 seconds, then shift, and so on).
- The student displays a positive to neutral facial expression.
  - The student displays any facial expression other than a frown.
- The student should have a "positive" tone of voice (enthusiastic, supportive, but not over-the-top).
- The student should state the peer's name when complimenting or cheering on the peer.

- The student makes a series of positive statements regarding the play of the peer (e.g., "Go, dude, go!" or "Way to go!") and at the appropriate time.
- These compliments are accented with gestures, such as arms raised, hand claps, and fist pumps.
- The student refrains from saying anything negative or using silly or nonsensical words.
- The student refrains from aggression throughout.
- The student stops cheering once the moment to do so appropriately has passed.

PHASE 3: Losing graciously. As necessary, instruction begins with discrimination training designed to teach the student the difference between losing appropriately (graciously) or inappropriately (being a sore loser or bad sport). The child is then taught the elements that make up losing graciously. The following task analysis can be used:

Once the student loses, then:

1. Face the opponent(s).
   - The student faces the opponent (orients his or her body and face toward the peer) the entire time.
1. Make eye contact.
   - The student initiates meaningful eye contact with the opponent (approximately 3 seconds).
2. The student has a neutral to positive facial expression,
   - Any facial expression is okay, other than a frown or a look of anger.
3. The student uses a neutral to positive voice tone.
   - The child's regular voice tone is appropriate.
4. The student maintains a relaxed body posture.
   - The student stands or sits up straight without any tenseness.
5. The student makes a general congratulatory statement (e.g., "Nice job," "Good game").
6. The student makes a specific compliment about the game (e.g., "I like the move you made").
7. If appropriate, the student can ask to play again sometime.
   - If the peer replies positively, play will occur again or the student makes a statement indicating acceptance and/or plans for future play.
   - If the peer replies negatively, the student will accept and leave.
8. The student refrains from whining or crying.
9. The student does not use negative words, statements, or silly or nonsensical words.
10. The student does not become aggressive in any way.
11. The student refrains from bragging, blaming, arguing, or making excuses.

PHASE 4: Being a team player. As in earlier phases, discrimination training and skill instruction focus on being a good teammate. Components may include, but are not limited to, the following:

- Not being a "ball hog" (i.e., being generous with the ball, passing when appropriate, giving others on the team an opportunity to participate more fully in the game)
- Learning to share equipment (e.g., letting others use baseball mitts if there aren't enough for a whole team)
- Knowing team positions and respecting others' ability to play their positions
- Letting someone play instead of you (i.e., substitutions, equity of playing time)
- Having patience for teammates' abilities and failings
- Knowing to cheer on teammates
- Knowing when and how to help a teammate improve his or her skills

PHASE 5: More on sportsmanship. As with earlier phases, discrimination training and skill instruction focus on learning to be an overall good sport and likable competitor, including the following considerations:

- Lining up to shake hands or give high fives to the opposing team after a game
- Shaking hands with the referees (if included in the competition)
- Refraining from taunting
- Refraining from commenting about opponents' shortcomings, failures, or losses
- Stopping play and helping an opposing team member who is injured

Responding to Teasing and Bullying

Objectives

- Better recognize situations involving undesirable peer interactions
- Better evaluate and respond to those situations in an effective, age-appropriate manner
- Discriminate between degrees of teasing and know how to respond accordingly
- Build confidence and comfort in social situations
- Develop awareness of others' intentions
- Develop self-advocacy skills

Prerequisites

- Cause and effect★
- Voice tone discrimination
- Basic inferences
- Understanding absurdities and incongruities
- Accurately reading nonverbal social cues

★*See A Work In Progress.*

Procedure

To begin teaching this critical social skill, discrimination training may be appropriate. Set up situations involving contrived in vivo examples, watching videotapes, reading written scenarios, observing naturally occurring events, and discussing recent or prior events. Presenting these scenarios in as natural and realistic a fashion as possible will facilitate better skill generalization. Importantly, this program can be run not only individually, but also in small groups or in large group settings. Teaching this skill systematically in group or classroom environments allows for practice with peers. Further, this approach creates greater potential for developing a group awareness and culture around the topic. For some students, using Teaching Interactions may be the most appropriate instruction tactic in this area.

PHASE 1: Increasing social awareness. The student discriminates between friendly comments and interactions and interactions involving a teasing or bullying element. The student becomes proficient in discerning the intent of a person engaged in the interaction. Examples may include the following:

NOT TEASING	TEASING/BULLYING
Friendly comments	Negative comments or comments with a negative tone
Polite conversatio	Enticements to engage in a potentially embarrassing or stigmatizing behavior
Appropriate questions	Pranks
Joking	Making fun of the person; verbal attacks

PHASE 2: The student discriminates between degrees of teasing, bullying, and risk. The following examples, while potentially applicable to a student, are also offered as starting points from which to generate individualized content. These individualizations should be based on the student, his or her personal experiences, and the settings and culture to which the skill is being applied.

- Mild teasing (deemed "not too big a deal" by the student/peer group norms)
  - No physical intimidation
  - Silly or nonpersonal comments
  - Making vocalizations (e.g., "Duh," "Ha!" "Eeew," "Ugh")
  - Mildly critical facial expressions or staring
  - Limited staring with mild laughing
- Moderate teasing (bothersome, slightly hurtful)
  - No physical intimidation
  - Insults (mean/offensive/personal)
  - Repetitive vocalizations intended to irritate or annoy
  - Making faces, staring, or laughing for a long duration
  - Writing notes and drawing pictures (mean/offensive/personal)
  - Enticement to engage in potentially embarrassing or stigmatizing behaviors
- Severe teasing and bullying ("big deal," prolonged, hurtful, potentially dangerous)
  - Physical intimidation (e.g., hurting someone, shoving, punching, kicking, twisting someone's arm)
  - Spitting
  - Throwing objects to hit or scare someone
  - Stalking
  - Stealing, hiding, or destroying belongings
  - Enticement to engage in a dangerous, risky, restricted, or illicit behavior
  - An aggressive, profane verbal barrage
  - Threats of violence, physical intimidation (e.g., "Do my homework or I'll get you after school"; threats can be spoken, gestural, or written)

PHASE 3: The student develops appropriate methods of dealing with teasing and bullying. This phase includes practicing a variety of effective and age-appropriate responses to teasing and bullying. Teaching Interactions for developing meaningful responses would be employed in this phase.

Examples of potential responses follow:

- Ignore the behavior/let it go
- Laugh it off
- Tease back (e.g., "As if you would know!", "Look who's talking")
- Tell person to stop (age-appropriate examples might include "Knock it off" or "Enough already!")
- Get someone (a friend, a teacher, or other adult)
- Surround yourself with "witnesses" (friends, buddies, and others, creating a potential chorus of "Knock it off" responses)
- Indicate you are annoyed
- Refrain from indicating you are annoyed
- Make a comment ("Whatever")
- Find something else to do
- Walk away

PHASE 4: Create response specificity. Present scenarios with teasing or bullying of varying intensities, degrees, and purposes. The student demonstrates or describes an appropriate response specific to the precursor. Be sure to include occasional examples of appropriate, friendly (or friendly joking) precursor scenarios as well, to allow for flexible and natural responding to a variety of realistic social situations.

PHASE 5: What if that doesn't work? The student problem solves and practices further responses when the first response to teasing or bullying is not effective. For example:

- The student ignores someone poking him or her in the back, but it continues.
- The student tells his or her friend of a threatening note from a bully; now the friend is getting threatening notes, too.
- A tease goes from "mild" to "moderate" to "severe."

PHASE 6: Develop greater awareness and understanding of how complex a provocative situation can be. The student learns to take into account contributing factors to determine the degree of a tease or provocation. The student learns to evaluate how the following factors influence the degree of intensity of the behavior. Present the child with a scenario involving one or more of the factors in the list below and ask him or her to evaluate the intensity of the behavior and the intent of the other person based on those factors. Then adjust the scenario by changing the factors. It is important to be systematic when altering the factors to ensure that the child understands how each factor can influence the situation.

- Location (school, home, and so on)
- Volume
- Proximity
- Body language
- Tone
- Number of onlookers
- Medium (Internet, written note, verbal)
- Relationship/familiarity with person
- Duration
- Frequency
- Intent (to embarrass, to intimidate)
- Age

PHASE 7: Promote response generality. Repeat the steps in Phases 4 and 5 using scenarios that include factors from the preceding list.

PHASE 8: Transfer teaching into the student's day. If teasing and bullying occur during the student's typical day, determine the student's ability to evaluate the situation and demonstrate the skills in the moment. If teasing or bullying occurs inconsistently, set up situations where a cohort teases or bullies the student. To reduce the contrived situation's negative consequences, inform the student ahead of time. Tell the student to expect teasing or bullying at some point in the day and to remember the skills he or she has learned. Initially, the teasing or bullying situation should occur shortly after the student is warned. Gradually, the time between informing the student and the incident itself should increase. Eventually, the student should receive no warning and be able to react appropriately.

Interrupting Others

Objectives

- Recognize when someone is busy in interaction and conversation
- Evaluate indicators of appropriate times to interrupt others
- Recognize circumstances under which interrupting is more or less appropriate
- Demonstrate a range of appropriate methods of interrupting, and apply these methods to different situations and audiences as the situation requires
- Accept a delay before interrupting others, and occupy self appropriately during this delay
- Refrain from interrupting when offers are refused or when interrupting has been occurring with too great a frequency

Prerequisites

- Frustration tolerance, impulse control, and waiting
- Assertiveness
- Environmental awareness (awareness of the presence of others)★
- Basic social initiation
- Reading basic nonverbal social cues
- Intermediate conversation and interactional skills★

★See *A Work In Progress.*

PHASE 1: Why interrupting is important and when to use it (recognizing when someone is busy). The focus of this phase is to provide the *why* and *when* of interrupting. The child is given rationales for appropriate interrupting skills and choices. Further effort is directed at teaching the child to identify when someone is busy versus available. Making this distinction will aid the child in evaluating exactly when interrupting skills need to be applied (i.e., if the individual is not occupied, then interrupting would not be occurring, and mere social initiation skills would be utilized).

    Step 1. Reasons for interrupting in an appropriate manner
        The child is provided with rationales for utilizing appropriate interruption skills and strategies as well as for the problematic results of inappropriate interrupting.

Rationales might include the following ideas:

- You are more likely to get what you want if you interrupt your parents in a way that doesn't upset or annoy them.
- It might actually get people to listen better and more quickly to you (because they stop and lecture you for bothering them when you interrupt in a poor way).

- People will listen when it's really important (because you won't have "cried wolf").
- People will stop ignoring you.
- You might get to join in more often,

Step 2. When to use interrupting: Are people busy?
> The child learns when to use interrupting tools, by discriminating if others are actually preoccupied in a task or conversation.

The child should be able to discriminate if someone is busy within situations like the following:

- Two adults are talking.
- Two adults are in proximity but not currently interacting.
- The teacher is talking to the class.
- The teacher is promoting unstructured discussion.
- The teacher is talking to another or small group of students.
- Two or more peers are talking to each other.
- Two or more peers are not talking to each other but are concentrating on what they are doing.
- Two or more peers are engaged in an unstructured conversational free-for-all.
- An adult or child is engaged in a preoccupying activity (without other people interacting).

> Create two conditions: "busy" and "not busy." Have the child watch other people either interacting or engaged in solitary activities (in role-play, on video, or in natural settings), representing the two possible conditions. At different moments during the observation, the child identifies whether an identified person is busy or not busy. The child should also explain how he or she knows the person is busy or not busy, so a bank of knowledge and generalized knowledge about the way people look when they are busy and what constitutes "busyness" is developed. This discrimination training would look something like this:

Example 1: Busy

TEACHER: "What do you think about that person now?"

STUDENT: "He looks busy."

TEACHER: "How do you know he's busy?"

STUDENT: "Because he's talking and looking at that other boy."

Example 2: Not busy

TEACHER: "Do you think he's busy or not busy now?"

STUDENT: "I think he's not busy."

TEACHER: "How do you know?"

STUDENT: "Because he's quiet and not really doing anything."

PHASE 2: Recognizing timing indicators, As in Phase 1, the child is taught through discrimination training to identify cues indicating that, when a person is busy, interrupting could be initiated. Cues include the following:

- Pause in or end of an activity
- Pause in conversation
- Invitation to interrupt offered by the individual
- Eye contact and positive facial expression or nonverbal positive acknowledgments offered by the individual

PHASE 3: Appropriateness indicators. As in the preceding phases, the child is taught through discrimination training to identify situations and cues that indicate interrupting statements or questions, in this situation, are more or less appropriate. Indicators taught could include the following:

- The child has information regarding an emergency to share. Specific examples of emergencies should be taught—such as the need to give aid to another—but rules of what constitutes emergencies should also be taught—such as that if action isn't taken right away, someone could be hurt—when possible.
- The other is doing an activity that should not be interrupted. Specific examples should be taught, but types of activities should also be provided if possible—such as emergencies, activities that require full and careful attention, or activities that require delicate action.
- The other has stated not to interrupt.
- The other is an adult in an authority position.
- Prior nonverbal cues to not interrupt have been offered. Specific nonverbal cues will likely need to be taught.
- Individuals who are talking have gone to a secluded area.
- Class rules have forbidden interrupting in specific situation.
- The child has off-topic or obsessive-theme-oriented information to share.
- The child has an accomplishment to share.
- A window of opportunity for action exists for the child.
- The child wants to socially join in a conversation, activity, or interaction with peers.

If capable, the child will need to learn to weigh indicators when more than one is present, so as to determine relative appropriateness of interrupting.

PHASE 4: Requisite interrupting related skills. These requisites should be instructed utilizing Teaching Interactions in simulations that gradually become increasingly challenging and realistic.

- Pausing before interrupting
  - The child may need to learn to pause (perhaps using self-talk or a mini relaxation moment—for example, taking a breath) before interrupting. This skill will be especially useful when the situation needs to be assessed by the child and skill element decisions need to be made (discussed later in this program). It becomes especially important when matters of urgency for the child are involved. Programming should gradually work toward increasing such challenges.

- Knowing waiting is required
  - The child may need to be taught, through discrimination training, when an approach has been accepted, denied, or just delayed (and waiting is required). Such recognition should be taught in response to verbalizations as well as to gestural cues (e.g., someone waving a palm up and down to indicate "wait," or putting an index finger up as sign to indicate that the child has been noticed but needs to "wait a minute").

- Waiting when interrupting is delayed
  - The child must often learn to tolerate a delay. Again, this skill becomes especially important when some urgency is involved. The child must also learn how to occupy such wait time, without resorting to self-stimulatory or odd responding (while remembering and retaining the motivation for and the content of the interruption).

- Refraining from finishing the interruption
  - On some occasions, the child may begin to interrupt, but then be interrupted himself or herself. In this scenario, the child must tolerate not being able to finish as well as be able to desist talking and interacting. Again, practice should be progressive and involve elements such as how long the child has been talking, how enthusiastic he or she is about the subject, and how important conveying the information is.

- Tolerating a denial
  - The child must learn to handle the scenario in which an attempt at interrupting is refused. Again, work should progress toward the inclusion of situations that involve matters of importance to the child.

- Knowing when and how to gain assistance
  - Through discrimination training and role-playing, the child should learn about situations that suggest assistance is necessary (for example, when interruptions are ignored or denied) and know who to ask (a teacher, an available adult, a close peer) for help (or guidance) when interrupting efforts are not successful.

PHASE 5: Interrupting skill elements. In this phase, the child learns a number of skill elements that can be used to interrupt other people. Through a Teaching Interaction approach (see Chapter 2), the child practices using these skills in a structured setting, to ensure success and fluent performance. Set up situations that require interrupting (e.g., two or more people are conversing or an individual is occupied with an engrossing activity). Incorporation of indicators learned in earlier phases will be necessary, and additional finer social cue discriminations may be required. Once the child has mastered one skill element, teach the others in a similar fashion.

- Waiting for a pause or end
  - The child should approach the person he or she wants to speak to, stand at an appropriate distance, wait until there is a pause in or completion of the conversation or activity, and then start speaking.
- Hand raising in class to interrupt
  - The child is taught (incorporating appropriateness indicators) to interrupt instructional staff during small- and large-group teaching arrangements. Noticing pauses in instruction or identification of topic transition points could be incorporated, for some students, into instruction of this element.
- Talking over the top
  - This skill element should be used only with appropriate other parties, such as siblings and known peers. It should be taught that such an approach makes sense with joining-in interrupting or when emergencies or urgent matters must be shared.
  - The child should approach the children he or she wants to speak to, stand at an appropriate distance, listen to the conversation and make sure he or she has something relevant or important to say, and then speak in a clear, loud (yet polite) voice while the others are still speaking.
- Making an interrupting statement
  - The child can be taught that this method can be used with adults, when someone is engaged in an activity or conversation, when topics other than those being discussed are to be shared, and when joining in is not the intent.
  - The child should wait for a pause in the conversation, and then make an interrupting statement in a polite voice, such as "Excuse me," "I have something I really need to ask," or "Sorry to interrupt." The child will need to correctly determine whether the other person has heard the statement. The child then assesses whether the person has offered affirmative acknowledgment (e.g., says, "Yes, can I help you?" or offers eye contact and an inquiring expression or, conversely, says, "Just a minute"). If affirmative acknowledgment is provided, the child should proceed with the interruption. If affirmative acknowledgment is not provided, the child should wait and to try again. If indicators are provided that interrupting is not appropriate, the child needs to end the interruption attempt and leave.
- Proximity, eye contact, and waiting
  - This method would most likely be used with adults when interruption is important but ongoing activities or conversations are also relatively engrossing, preoccupying, or important. These scenarios would also be situations that are unlikely to contain frequent pauses and for which interrupting statements would not be indicated.

- The child is taught to approach the person he or she wishes to interrupt and stand for a brief period (not longer than 30 seconds) at a comfortable proximity. During that time, the child orients toward the other person, attempting to make eye contact. A facial expression containing inquiring, permission-requesting, and/or hopeful elements can be taught to the child to be utilized should eye contact be provided by the other person. If positive acknowledgment is provided, then the child can proceed with the interruption. The child is taught to leave within 30 seconds if no eye contact is given (as well as in response to direct verbal and nonverbal refusals to be interrupted).

PHASE 6: Evaluating and choosing the best skill to use. Once the child has learned the range of interrupting skill elements, he or she still needs to evaluate when and how to use these skills in everyday life. This consideration includes deciding which skill to try first and changing the skills utilized depending on the setting and people involved.

1. Deciding which skill to use first

    This step involves the child making decisions, based on the variables and indicators listed previously as well as unfolding circumstances in the interaction, about which skill element to use. It is analogous to "Wh discriminations" (see *A Work in Progress*) in which separate components are taught first (e.g., who, what, where) and then a program is used to teach the child to make discriminations (and choices) about which component applies.
    The program should initially use contrived scenarios (video, role-play, or historical examples) in which the child must make a decision about only one variable (e.g., adult or child). Over time, more choice indicators are included until complicated situations are constructed (e.g., a well-known adult is engaged in an important but loud activity, and the child has urgent question to ask; a lesson started as a lecture but has evolved into a class discussion). The objective is for the child to make a decision based on the variables present in the scenario and then choose those skill elements that appear most fitting.

2. Changing the choice of interrupting skill based on the situation
    The second part of this phase adds further complication to skill element utilization. In some situations, additional decisions need to be made concerning the use of interruption skill elements—for example, if a child, still needing to interrupt, should tone it down or boost it up; or if the attempt to interrupt is rebuffed, whether to try again immediately, try again later, or forego the interruption).

Some examples follow:

- An adult on the phone has not responded to the child's attempt to convey an important message
- Peers looked very annoyed when the child tried to talk over them to join in and the peers are not the most preferred
- A familiar, preoccupied adult has not responded to proximity and waiting and the question needs to be answered within the hour
- When the two people talking paused, the child tried to interrupt and join in and ask a question, but the others just resumed chatting

PHASE 7: Amount of interrupting. Using appropriate skills to interrupt may not be the only need demonstrated by a child: The child may need to regulate how often or much he or she interrupts.

This need may depend partially on the reaction of the other people involved. If the people being interrupted are getting annoyed by the frequency of interruptions, then it's time to tone it down. It may also depend on the setting and the extent to which the interrupting is disrupting or interfering with (or interrupting) the activities involved. In general, amount of interruption pertains not only to interruptions within a single conversation, but also to interruptions of the same person or within the same setting over a number of days or weeks.

Discrimination training should occur around the reaction of others, over time when a sequence of interruptions has occurred. Signs of annoyance or frustration in others (e.g., rolling eyes, sighing, frequent statements by a parent to "stop interrupting and let other people have a turn") should be included with repeated occurrences. Further, the child should be taught to anticipate what the likely reaction would be to additional interruption in response to differing amounts of prior interruptions (e.g., "What do you think might happen if they were interrupted again?" or "Do you think she'll be happy to hear an interruption again?")

Additional discrimination work should involve noting when certain levels of interruptions begin to interfere with the performance of certain tasks and activities in a range of settings. This effort can be combined with work that was done in Phase 3, teaching that in some circumstances even a small amount of interrupting is inappropriate.

Efforts in this phase should be combined with work focusing on teaching the child to monitor his or her own level of interrupting.

PHASE 8: Generalization. Although skill instruction has occurred in increasingly complex fashion, this phase involves transfer to naturally occurring situations. Effort needs to be directed toward working utilization of skills into real-life situations. Chapter 2 on Teaching Interactions covers generalization protocols. In addition, the following areas should be considered as work moves the child from contrived training to everyday, naturally occurring situations:

- From familiar and preferred individuals to less known or preferred individuals
- From comfortable, familiar situations to less familiar circumstances
- From priming to no prior reminders or preparation
- From situations in which the interrupting interaction occurs in relative isolation to circumstances in which many other activities are occurring simultaneously
- From neutral content areas to more important or urgent (to the child) matters
- From simple, straightforward situations requiring interrupting to those with several and possibly conflicting variables and indicators
- From more responsive and supportive reactions to interruption to less receptive or even antagonistic responses

Gaining Attention Through Problem Solving ("If at First You Don't Succeed, Try, Try Again")

Objectives

- Gain attention appropriately
- Get attention from people in different relationship categories
- Get needs met and deal with urgent situations
- Increase persistence
- Increase problem-solving and critical-thinking skills

Prerequisites

- Attributes★
- Social awareness★
- Perspective taking
- General knowledge and reasoning★

★See *A Work in Progress.*

Procedure

This program teaches the student problem-solving skills. Specifically, the student learns to be persistent when the initial attempt to gain another person's attention is not effective. The student also learns to identify possible ways to adjust attention-seeking behavior and apply it to a variety of situations. This endeavor will involve demonstration of both problem-solving skills and persistence. The types of problems should be individualized to the student and should be directly related to the type of errors the child demonstrates.

PHASE 1: Identifying when a problem has occurred while attempting to initiate communication. In this phase, the student is told which initiation aspect to evaluate (e.g., "Tell me if (cohort) is being loud enough to get someone's attention"). The student observes role-plays or videotaped interactions and identifies whether a problem exists within the attempted interaction initiation.

Possible problems to consider include the following:

- The speaker is talking too quietly.
- The other person is too far away.
- The speaker is not facing the listener.

- The other person is busy.
- The speaker has not identified who he or she is talking to.
- The other person is talking.

Strategy 1: The student responds by using cards labeling the problematic behavior and the appropriate behavior (e.g., "Too quiet" and "Loud enough" are written on cards).

Strategy 2: The student either identifies the problem verbally or indicates the person was effectively communicating (student says, "She is looking the wrong way" or "she looked at peer").

PHASE 2: Discrimination of communication difficulties. In this phase, the student is instructed to identify which aspect of the communication attempt is problematic.

- Instructor: "Let's see if you can figure out what's going wrong."
- The student watches and evaluates a scenario, and then says: "That person is busy and isn't listening" or "He isn't facing her."

Initially, if the student experiences difficulty assessing what to focus on (based on what is being watched, or if more than one component is being expressed in the scenario), providing a written or pictorial list of the salient components may be helpful. This prompt should be faded as quickly as possible.

PHASE 3: Adjusting communicative behavior to address the potential problem. The student learns to identify how to adjust behavior based on the identified problem component and practices implementing the solution. Consider the following examples:

- Listener is too far away $\rightarrow$ Speaker can move closer
- Speaker is too quiet $\rightarrow$ Speaker can increase volume
- Speaker isn't facing the listener $\rightarrow$ Speaker adjusts, faces listener

Step 1: The student observes a role-play and suggests solutions to the person initiating the interaction (e.g., the student instructs the speaker to "Move closer so he can hear you").

Step 2: The student is involved in the role-play and must change his or her own behavior.

PHASE 4: What do I do now? What if the listener does not respond to the initial communicative attempt? The student problem-solves this situation and comes up with alternative ways to gain attention. These alternatives will vary based on the relationship between the listener and the student and on the location where the communication occurs (i.e., at school, at home, in the community, or somewhere else).

- Peer as listener
  - Repeat the peer's name.
  - Repeat the communicative attempt (i.e., question, request, comment).
  - Talk even louder.
  - Tap the peer on the shoulder (or use some other nonverbal, physically appropriate method of getting attention).
  - Use age-appropriate humor or sarcasm (e.g., "Yoo-hoo, I'm talking to you!" or "What are you, deaf?").
  - Use a more insistent tone.
  - If warranted (due to the urgency of the peer having to listen), threaten to inform an adult.
- Grown-up as listener (see the "Interrupting Others" program for additional ideas)
  - Say, "Excuse me" or "Pardon me."
  - If the target listener is talking to someone else, wait for a pause in the conversation.
  - If the listener is busy, wait until a break occurs or the "business" is completed.
  - Repeat the listener's name.
  - Repeat the communicative attempt (i.e., question, request, comment) with a louder voice.
  - Find another available adult.

PHASE 5: Discriminating emergency or urgent situations requiring attention. Following a description of a scenario, the student indicates whether the situation is "urgent" or "not urgent." Consider the following examples:

Urgent
- You or someone else is hurt
- Someone is in danger
- You really need to use the toilet
- You need a tissue urgently
- You are feeling sick and might vomit
- There is a fire, flood, or household emergency
- You have been asked to get someone else urgently

Not Urgent
- You want to show the teacher your work
- You have a question
- You need to use the toilet, but can wait
- You want to share something funny
- You want to ask if you can turn on the TV

PHASE 6: Problem solving how to best get someone's attention when a situation is urgent. The student learns how to get attention when in an urgent situation and practices this behavior in role-play situations. Once proficiency is displayed, the type of situation should be randomized between urgent and non-urgent situations. Examples of appropriate attention getting when the situation is urgent include the following:

- Interrupt the other person
- Tell the person right away why you need attention
- Persist in giving information
- Say, "It's important!"

PHASE 7: Program for skill generality. Create opportunities for the student to practice this skill in the natural environment. It is important to provide opportunities to practice each of the variables learned in earlier phases, creating a whole skill set. The test of mastery in this skill area is whether the student can develop new alternatives in novel (as well as everyday) situations. To ensure that this goal is met, practice in this stage should include use of a problem-solving template, applied to gaining attention. Such a template could include the following elements:

- Identify the reason why attention seeking is not working
- Determine the urgency
- Consider solutions
- Factor in important considerations
- Try a solution
- Evaluate the solution's success and try again (reviewing prior steps as necessary)

Secrets

Objectives

- Develop the ability to make social judgments
- Develop authentic peer relationships
- Increase the likelihood of successful social interactions
- Develop decision-making and problem-solving skills
- Increase self-awareness
- Develop critical-thinking skills

Prerequisites

- Joint attention
- Theory of mind
- Cause and effect★
- Understanding of inferences
- Understanding emotions (simple and complex)★
- Impulse control

★See *A Work in Progress.*

Procedure

For better or for worse, secrets are a part of most youth (and social) cultures. To understand and operate in an individual's social world, facility in the area of secrets is necessary. With awareness and some skill, the student can ultimately decide the degree to which he or she participates in the secret-keeping and -telling interactions of his or her social environment.

PHASE 1A: The student is able to identify what a secret is. The student learns to identify the characteristics of a secret. This process will assist in identifying what is and is not secret information. For the purpose of this phase, a *secret* is defined as "information that not everybody knows, and there is a reason not everybody knows."

Understanding what a secret is can be taught through discrimination training. For example, write the following descriptions on separate file cards:

- Is a secret
- Is not a secret

The student then holds up the appropriate card when scenarios are presented.

To help the student more fully understand the concept, the discriminations should be obvious initially, but then become more subtle. Some examples of obvious discriminations follow:

- The Fourth of July is a holiday.
    - "Is not a secret" (culturally, publicly shared information)
- Jonny's being given a surprise birthday party.
    - "Is a secret" (it's a surprise; Jonny should not be told)

Other potential discriminations include the following scenarios:

Is a Secret	Is Not a Secret
John doesn't like (*person*).	I am wearing black pants.
Susan cheated on a test.	We had a math test today.
Beth is throwing a surprise party for Bobby.	There is often cake at parties.

Less obvious may be secrets that are more similar to more commonly held information:

- There's a quiz in Ms. Palos' Spanish class tomorrow.
    - "Is not a secret" (all the students have likely been told; if a student was absent, this would be information to share)
- There's a *pop* quiz in Ms. Palos' Spanish class tomorrow.
    - "Is a secret" (only the teacher should know; the definition of "pop quiz" is that is it a surprise, or secret).

More difficult discriminations may involve information that not everyone knows but there is no reason or purpose behind that fact, or situations where, for deliberate reasons, some know and some do not know the same information:

Is a Secret	Is Not a Secret
The surprise party guest list is a secret kept from Bobby.	Those on the guest list know they are invited to the surprise party.
Dan has a crush on Kayla.	Dan doesn't like green beans.
Suzie is afraid of water.	Kayla is afraid of muggers.

PHASE 1B: The student identifies why information is secret. This understanding is critical and is a prerequisite to further social teaching. By developing this knowledge, the student can cultivate a respect for privacy, can better develop trust with friends, and will be less likely to become socially stigmatized. In this phase, the student learns reasons why information can or cannot be shared, and why something is secret versus just being information someone doesn't know. Have the student give reasons why information may truly be secret. This understanding can be taught using the student's own experiences or by the student inferring why generated examples may be secrets. The following list may assist in creating more rationales for why information may be private or a secret:

Possible Reasons to Keep a Secret

- To avoid getting in trouble (e.g., broke something, cheated, disobeyed a parent)
- To avoid hurting someone's feelings (e.g., not enjoying food that someone made, not liking a gift that someone gave you)
- To surprise someone (e.g., a party, an event, a promotion)
- To avoid embarrassment (e.g., got your period in class, made a mistake)
- To form a bond with someone by having something you share with them (e.g., gossip)
- The time for people to know has not yet arrived (e.g., not sure if you got the part in a play yet)
- To avoid a confrontation

PHASE 1C: The student identifies from whom the secret is being kept. A possible way to introduce this concept is to provide examples of secrets—including the rationales why the information is a secret—with the student and then to identify who could be told the information and who could not.

Example: "I bought hockey tickets for Jason and myself but want it to be a surprise for him."

- The student identifies the secret's rationale. (It's a surprise.)
- The student identifies who this secret should be kept from. (It would be a secret from Jason, but the list of people not told may include other people, such as his friends or people who may inadvertently tell him.)

PHASE 2: Discriminating between "shared" and "private" secrets. Some secrets are shared with one or several others. Other secrets are personal and may have one other person privy to the information or, at times, no other people. The student learns to discriminate between these distinctive informational categories.

Both shared and private secrets are, by definition, secrets. The distinction depends on whether the secret is known by a group or by just one individual. In the case of private secrets, typically only the individual knows, and possibly a professional (e.g., a psychologist or a doctor), family members, or a truly trusted friend. Further, private secrets are typically extremely personal in nature, such as whether someone has a medical or psychological diagnosis or has undergone a medical procedure.

PHASE 3: How to tell and how to receive secrets. The student should know how to react when told a secret and how to properly tell a secret.

- Telling a secret
  - The student must be aware of who the secret is to be kept from.
  - The student must be aware of others to keep the secret from so the information does not get to the central person.

- Delivery must be discreet:
  - Information should not be overheard by others (vocal volume).
  - The secret may be delivered when there are few others around (draw as little attention to the interaction as possible).
  - The student must make clear the nature of the secret (e.g., cannot be shared; don't tell specific people).
- Receiving a secret
  - The student remains as discreet as possible (no over-reaction to the information; no verbal outbursts).
  - The student must show interest.
  - The student must acknowledge the "importance" of the information so the teller feels secure about the secret being kept.

PHASE 4: When to keep a secret. This phase involves ensuring secrets are not kept that are potentially harmful to the student or others if the information is not shared or exposed. It involves teaching a student to identify the consequences of keeping versus telling the secret and then making a judgment as to whether the secret should be kept.

The teacher sets up a scenario or vignette. Within this situation, the student identifies consequences of telling versus keeping information secret. It is important that the student identifies real consequences, likely affecting the student's or others' lives. If necessary (for greater understanding and comprehension), the consequences can be divided into positives and negatives. The student then weighs the pros and cons and decides whether to tell the information or keep it secret.

Consider the following example:

- Brenda cheated on her math test and told you; she also told you not to tell anyone else. What would happen if you told the teacher that Brenda cheated? What would happen if you didn't tell?
  - The student ponders:
    - Brenda broke the rules.
    - If I don't tell, I will feel mad.
    - Brenda should be punished.
    - If I tell, Brenda won't tell me any more secrets.
    - Brenda will be mad at me.
    - Brenda may get a detention.
    - We won't be able to hang out after school.
  - The student weighs the pros and cons and makes a decision.

If the student is unable to make a decision using these strategies, then definite reasons or criteria should be provided for determining when to tell or expose a secret. No matter what, clear rules should be established regarding the sharing of information related to sexual abuse, physical abuse, dangerous behavior, breaking the law, bullying behavior, and harmful actions.

PHASE 5: When a secret is no longer a secret. Teach the student to identify the circumstances in which a secret may no longer need to be kept or is no longer a secret. This may occur for a variety of reasons:

- The secret may be time limited (for example, you need to keep a secret about a surprise party only until the party happens).
- The people to whom the secret is important may change their minds.
- The secret may be found out or told by others, so that it is no longer a secret.

Again, use experiences from the student's life, scenarios, or vignettes, with the student identifying when a secret no longer is a secret. Consider these examples:

- The teacher tells the student, "I am going to give Bella a Barbie as a present at her birthday party."
  - Is this a secret now?
  - After Bella's birthday party, is it still a secret?
- Jenna tells you she likes Gary.
  - Is it still a secret?
  - If Jenna tells Gary she likes him, is it still a secret?

PHASE 6: How do you keep a secret? Once the student has decided a secret should be kept, actually keeping the secret may need to be taught. Considerations may include the following:

- Not advertising the secret
- Learning to change the topic when the subject of the secret comes up
- Learning to avoid the topic of the secret
- Lying if asked directly about the secret (the student needs to be able to identify what the consequences of this lie would be first)
- Practicing impulse control
- Identifying who may be a safe person to tell the secret to (i.e., a person who is not connected to the person who the secret is about)

Sharing

Objectives

- Develop better interaction skills
- Increase the potential for meaningful peer interactions
- Increase social motivation
- Develop tolerance

Prerequisites

- Frustration tolerance
- Awareness of peers★

★See *A Work in Progress.*

Procedure

This program is directed at various levels and aspects of behavior that pertain to sharing. Some early phases are quite basic and would be appropriate for students of even minimal capabilities. Later phases represent more advanced skill and capacity development, involve more sophisticated instructional techniques (i.e., Teaching Interactions; see Chapter 2), and are more appropriate for individuals of higher capability.

PHASE 1A: Building a positive connotation of "sharing." Often students hear the word "share" when their possessions or favorite snacks are being given to other people, and consequently associate a negative connotation with the idea of sharing. The goal of this phase is to have the student associate sharing with positive feelings. To do so, the teacher sets up situations where the student gets something he or she desires because a peer is asked to share with him. For example (peers who have a high probability of sharing should be chosen as partners):

- A peer may have a toy the student likes. When the student shows interest, the peer is asked to share with the student.
- A peer may have some food the student wants. When the student shows interest, the peer is asked to share with the student.
- The student is asked to do a chore or less preferred activity. A peer is then asked to help share the responsibility with the student, making the job easier.

During these activities, the teacher will label the "sharing" repeatedly so the student associates the word and action of "sharing" with a positive result.

PHASE 1B: Building the desire to share. Depending on the skills of the individual student, this phase may not be done initially. Some students may not require it at all, whereas others may need it teased out and focused on more intensely. Designed for students with good receptive language skills, this phase involves providing a rationale for why sharing is positive. Teaching this skill can occur in several ways:

- The teacher should converse about and highlight the positive results that sharing has garnered for the student. This conversation can focus on previous experiences, current examples, and predictions for future sharing.
- Rationales should be meaningful and individualized to each student. With that caveat in mind, other rationales can include the following:
  - "Things are more fun when you share them."
  - "Work can be less difficult or take less time when you share the responsibility."
  - "You get back a lot [people share with you] when you share with others."
- Associate "sharing" with other labels to which the student already has assigned a positive connotation:
  - "You shared! Cool, dude!"
  - "Wow, sharing is such a first-grade thing to do!" (with a student in kindergarten or beginning the first grade in school)
  - "Sharing the job got it done faster! Now you can take a break!"
- Pair sharing with highly preferred activities or tangibles:
  - "Hey, let's watch *Spiderman* and share some popcorn."

PHASE 2: Facilitated sharing: Understanding and tolerance. The student learns to share in situations facilitated by an adult. In this phase, the student is taught to follow an instruction requiring sharing with someone. For some students, this skill may simply be to learn what the instruction means; for others, learning to tolerate sharing with another person is the target skill.

Creating a "situation hierarchy" may be necessary to complete this phase. This approach will make the teaching more systematic and increase the likelihood the student will tolerate sharing in increasingly difficult situations. The hierarchy should begin with situations in which the student is highly likely to accept sharing and then progress to those situations in which it is extremely difficult for the student to share. "Sharing" in this phase consists of the student giving up something he or she has to another person.

Once someone has expressed interest in what the student has, the teacher prompts the student to both attend to this request or desire and act on it by actually sharing (giving the item to the peer). As soon as the item is shared, the student should be heavily reinforced. Pair external reinforcement with praise (i.e., "Look how happy you've made (peer's name)!" or "Sharing makes things easier for everyone!").

- Be sure to systematically fade prompts to notice/attend to the sharing request and actually share the item.
- Progress systematically through the hierarchy; treat it as an exercise in frustration tolerance and be patient.
- Be sure to include sharing unpleasant or less preferred tasks and activities in the hierarchy.

- As often as possible, find situations supporting sharing (for example, sharing was much more fun than doing the activity solo) to further assist in tolerance training.

Consider the following example:

- The student has a bag of chips. A peer enters and says, "I love chips!"
  - If student doesn't respond, the teacher can say, "It would be nice to share your chips." (A more intrusive prompt can be provided if needed to have the student to offer the bag.)
  - As the student offers the bag, praise him or her: "Nice sharing! (Peer) loves chips!"
  - Pair this action with reinforcement. If possible, set up the situation so that the peer then offers something desirable to the student. This tactic will highlight the reciprocity of sharing, again making it worth the student's while.

Initially, these situations should occur repeatedly in a short time period and, therefore, need to be arranged. It would not be advisable to initially rely on opportunities occurring incidentally, as such randomness will not provide enough chances for practice (especially given the need for practice to be progressive). Over time, more naturally occurring sessions can be included.

The following factors may affect a student's willingness to share:

- Having to share an entire toy or object versus a portion of a toy or object (e.g., taking turns playing with a light saber versus giving another person half a set of Lego blocks)
- The value of the item shared
- Whether the toy or object to be shared is owned by the student, owned by the peer, or not owned by either party
- Whether sharing has a permanent (sharing a cookie) or temporary result (sharing a toy that the student will eventually get back)
- Sharing with an adult versus sharing with a peer
- Giving up something for a short versus long period of time
- Sharing where enjoyment can still be derived while the other person has a turn (i.e., playing a videogame; watching another person play and cheering him or her on)

PHASE 3A: Student-initiated sharing. Once sharing is tolerated without protest or other disruptive behavior, the teacher should begin work on the student initiating sharing independently. This can be accomplished in a similar manner to Phase 2. One of the primary objectives of this phase is to fade the prompts to attend and respond to the request to share. Fading can include movement to within-stimulus prompts. In this case, the prompting would come from the peer and the communication and other indicators that sharing is appropriate would be emphasized.

- Initially the phrases can be obvious ("Can I have one?").
- As the student develops awareness and proficiency, more subtle phrases and behaviors should be introduced ("I love chips!"; "I need some more red blocks"; pairing a phrase such as "That's cool!" with a longing look at what the student has).

As an alternative to external prompting, priming and prime fading may be utilized. This approach would involve the student being reminded prior to the opportunity to share. Gradually, these reminders would become less frequent and would occur further in advance of sharing opportunities.

Shaping procedures can also be used as an alternative to prompting to increase a student's independent initiation of sharing. For example, the student might initially be reinforced for noticing that a peer wants something and allowing that person to take it; over time, the student would receive a higher level of reinforcement for offering the item.

Work should also focus on the sharing response offered by the student. Notably, the student's response may appear or sound rote.

- This issue needs to be addressed by using training and differential reinforcement focusing on different ways of presenting the skill.
- Teach students with expressive language to more fully respond with a variety of appropriate comments in addition to the physical action of sharing.

PHASE 3B: To share or not to share. On some occasions, not sharing is perfectly fine. The teacher should set up situations assisting in the student in making such discriminations. Some examples include the following scenarios:

- Sharing may actually take away the value of the activity or object.
- The person wanting to share never reciprocates.
- The student is being coerced rather than being an active participant in sharing.
- The "sharing" is permanent and there is no possibility of replacement.

Sharing Information and Experiences

There are many other examples and definitions of sharing, separate from the physical act of sharing materials, objects, and reinforcers. For example, sharing information or personal experiences with friends is a cornerstone of social connectedness. This type of sharing is actually a secondary reinforcer for many people—that is, something valued as a part of a relationship. Information sharing between friends can validate a response to a personal experience. For example, if a person is scared of a snake, turning to see how others react when a snake is near or talking about this fear with a peer can be validating and normalizing.

Sharing experiences can also result in support from friends and could alleviate or reduce emotional distress so that potential solutions can be sought. Further, sharing may amplify a positive emotional response when there is good news and may provide means for further interaction or connection during positive experiences. For example, if a person watches a movie with a friend, he or she has someone to share the scary parts with, to talk with during boring parts, and to discuss the movie with afterwards. Sharing information (at appropriate levels) with others online (on social media sites such as Facebook) may be an age-appropriate way to connect with others as well. Sharing experiences may promote connected emotional responses such as feelings of sympathy, joy, or empathy. More simply, sharing experiences or information may make us feel closer to someone because we have more in common.

When teaching sharing experiences and information, realize that the student may initially learn to share as a means to receive extrinsic (and possibly artificial) reinforcement. However, this point should not be the end of the teaching. Many students can be taught to share information and experiences for the same intrinsic reasons identified previously. This is a process, however, and should be understood as such.

PHASE 4A: Sharing information. Initially, teach the student to share information where the act of sharing results in consequences directly related to the information shared. As the student shows proficiency in sharing this information, move toward teaching sharing information where the relationship between the information and the consequence of sharing becomes less direct. Examples include the following scenarios:

- The student shares information about needs.
  - The student shares that he feels thirsty; the person he shares with offers to get him a drink.
  - The student shares she can't reach something; the person she shares with offers to get the item.
- The student shares information about preferences.
  - Student shares that he likes The Beatles; the person lends a Beatles CD.
  - The student shares that she doesn't like chocolate; the person brings treats later that don't include chocolate and emphasizes that it was remembered the student didn't like chocolate.
- The student shares information about interests.
  - The student shares information about a preferred topic; the other person provides student with new information about that topic.
  - The student shares information about liking an activity—for example, World Cup soccer matches. The other person says he loves this sport as well, and invites the student over to watch the game in 3D.

In the preceding examples, natural reinforcement is used. In some cases, however, external reinforcement may be required. This will increase the level of available reinforcement and, ideally, will increase the frequency of sharing information. Over time, the artificial reinforcement should be systematically faded to natural reinforcement.

PHASE 4B: Sharing experiences. Initially, make sure the student shares experiences that are greatly enriched when shared, so that the natural value of sharing experiences is emphasized. Some examples of shared experiences follow:

- The student engages in preferred activities that are otherwise less enjoyable when done solo.
  - Examples include paint ball, water fights, and building a human pyramid—all activities that are enhanced (or made possible) when carried out with another.

- The teacher sets up situations in which sharing reduces the negative aspects or consequences of an activity.
  - For example, sharing a chore reduces the workload and time spent on the drudgery; sharing a cab reduces the money you have to spend for the same trip; and sharing a pizza is cheaper if you cannot eat the whole thing by yourself anyway.

As the student progresses, the consequences related to sharing the activity will be less immediately experienced and possibly less obvious to the student. For example, sharing a movie with a friend may become reinforcing later when the student has someone to talk to about the movie. Initially, the teacher may have to review or point out these contingencies, so that the student is aware of the value of the shared experience. In time, such discussions should be faded, as the natural benefits of shared experience maintain such connected responding.

SOCIAL
LEARNING

Social Imitation

Objectives

- Attend to others' behaviors
- Build a foundation skill required in more natural educational settings
- Develop age-appropriate social behavior
- Develop a means to cue appropriate responding
- Increase breadth and length of environmental attending
- Increase social awareness
- Teach skills required for building social desire, interests, and influence
- Develop opportunities for increased social interaction
- Extract information from a group

Prerequisites

- Basic observational learning (e.g., "Do that," "Do what Mommy is doing")★
- Basic environmental and social awareness★
- Tolerance of peer proximity
- Basic inferences (for the last phase)

★See *A Work in Progress.*

Procedure

This program is an extension of the imitation and observational learning programs described in *A Work in Progress.* Involving the use of Discrete Trial Teaching, it is designed to focus on expanding and refining the group and social aspects of imitation skills.

PHASE 1: The student learns more expansive imitation. The student imitates a group of people, all of whom are performing an action simultaneously (e.g., in the classroom setting, the student imitates others banging drums).

PHASE 2: The student learns to imitate based on more subtle cues. To build better attending to detail, the student observes and then imitates a group of people who are engaging in subtle behavior. Examples include a group sitting with arms crossed, a group sitting and leaning forward, and a whole group looking at a door or window.

PHASE 3: The student learns to discriminate and copy more specifically. The student imitates a specific response characteristic or quality within a group. For example:

- Copy the loudest behavior
- Copy the "weirdest" behavior
- Copy the quietest people in the group

PHASE 4: The student follows conditional imitations. For example:

- "Do what the boys are doing"
- "Do what most people are doing"
- "Don't do what your sister is doing"

PHASE 5: The student incorporates social inferencing into imitations. Social judgments and inferences come in to play during this phase. For example:

- "Do what your mom would like"
- "Do what your friends think is cool"
- "Follow the rule"

Information Seeking

Objectives

- Ask questions to determine what is occurring in different social situations
- Use pertinent, salient questions to gather specific social information
- Discriminate questions appropriate to specific social situations to gain relevant social information

Prerequisites

- Basic observational learning skills★
- Question asking★

★See *A Work in Progress.*

Procedure

This program teaches a student to ask questions, thereby gaining the information needed to enter a social situation, to get needs and desires met in social situations, or to acquire social learning. The teaching techniques should match the student's skill level, but can include a mix of Discrete Trial Teaching and Teaching Interactions. A combination of discrimination training, role-play, and practice in the natural environment should be utilized to promote generalization and greater skill independence.

PHASE 1: Situation discrimination. The student learns to discriminate whether the required information can be acquired simply through observation or whether additional information must be sought. This phase is strictly for discrimination training; it does not include teaching which questions to ask or how to better enter a social situation. The student should simply consider the questions "Can I tell what's going on just by watching?" and "Should I ask what's going on?" An example of this discrimination follows:

- *Observational situation:* A bell is ringing, people are walking in a specific direction, and the student smells smoke. Through the use of observation, the student should know to follow the group.
- *Additional information needed:* The student sees a group of peers walking quickly toward the school playground. There are no other environmental cues to assist the student in deciding what to do. The student will need to ask, "Where is everyone going?" or "What are you all doing?", to determine whether to follow.

PHASE 2: Asking the right question. In a structured teaching setting, the student learns to use different questions to obtain specific information. Situations requiring the student to seek information may include the following scenarios:

- The student cannot identify who to obtain something from ("Who should I ask for a pen and paper?")
- The student wants to know what is being discussed ("What are you guys talking about?")
- The student wants to know what a group is doing ("Hey, what are you up to?")
- The student wants to play, but cannot figure out the activity's rules ("How do you play this?")
- There are several activities occurring and the student has to choose one ("I want to play kick-ball! Whose team can I be on?")
- The student observes a dramatic event such as a fight or people moving away quickly ("Is everything okay?")

PHASE 3: Discriminating immediacy and urgency. The student learns to determine whether something is dangerous or serious and how to gather information in those situations. Also, situations teaching the student the concept of "missed opportunities" are presented; in other words, if the student does not act or gather more information, the opportunity will be lost.

PHASE 4: Who is appropriate to ask? The student learns to determine who to ask by evaluating several factors, including the student's relationship with the other person, the other person's availability, the type information needed, the other person's expertise, and the situation requiring student to ask in the first place. Considerations include the following issues:

- The student's familiarity with the person
- The person's role in the situation (e.g., teacher, parent, authority figure, peer, professional acquaintance)
- The nearness or proximity of the person (Who is closest and, therefore, easiest to ask?)
- The person's availability
- The specifics of the situation

PHASE 5: Generalized application of skills. Through structured in vivo teaching opportunities, the student learns to ask questions based on a variety of situations. If needed, timing and fluency of questions are addressed.

PHASE 6: Review and follow-up. The student evaluates the information given to the questions asked. He or she determines if enough information was given to know what to do. If not, the student asks more detailed follow-up questions. This phase ensures that the student completely understands the needed information and can more confidently respond or act in specific situations.

PHASE 7: Generalization. Learning from previous phases is generalized to more natural situations. Ultimately, the student learns to evaluate situations and seek information as necessary (opportunities occur more intermittently and unpredictably).

Flow of Group Social Play (Stay with/Follow a Friend)

Objectives

- Increase participation in social situations
- Increase social interest
- Develop flexibility in play and leisure activities
- Increase observational learning skills
- Increase the ability to transition within the social domain

Prerequisites

The student should be able to engage in parallel and or interactive play with at least one peer across a number of activities. The student can be learning other social play and peer interaction skills concurrently with this program. Other programmatic requisites include the following:

- Joint attention skills
- Beginning observational learning (i.e., can successfully "do that;" notices what peers are doing)*
- Social imitation
- Knowledge of peer names*

*See *A Work in Progress.*

Procedure

This program promotes social awareness and peer-following behavior in a student. It is also designed to increase social interest based on peer presence, as opposed to student interest being specifically and solely related to an activity. The goal is to teach the student to observe a peer playing, participate in that play, notice if the peer transitions to a different type of play, and follow that peer to the new activity. Reinforcement should target the student's attention, observation of the peer, and successful transition (by following the peer) to next activity.

The teacher should create a play and leisure activity hierarchy ranging from highly preferred to neutral to nonpreferred (but not despised). As the student progresses through the teaching phases, this hierarchy forms the basis of the instructional sequence. The student should begin the learning with activities classified as "nonpreferred" (because attention to peer and transition to another activity will be easiest to establish with these activities) and, as the skill develops, should move on to activities that are more difficult to transition from. As is most often the case, preferences change—sometimes daily—and many factors contribute to something becoming less or more preferred. Thus the hierarchy will need occasional updating to remain relevant to the teaching.

Prompting Strategies

Use within-stimulus prompting to more effectively draw the student's attention and set up more independent observational skills. For this program, within-stimulus prompts may include very obvious engagement by peers in play activities or very obvious switches from activity to activity. For example, while coloring, the peer may jam the markers deliberately into the container, signaling an end to the activity. Similarly, when transitioning to building with Lego blocks, the emphasis prompt may include spilling out all the blocks in a very exaggerated and loud fashion.

PHASE 1: Transition in structured, adult-led situations. This phase involves watching an adult and deciding whether to transition with that person. Within-stimulus prompts are ideal for this phase.

> Step 1: The student observes the teacher's behavior and discriminates whether to transition based on the teacher's actions
>
> The teacher and student participate in parallel or interactive play (on the activity hierarchy, begin with nonpreferred and neutral activities). The teacher uses within-stimulus prompts as necessary, by making an exaggerated, obvious play or transition action. The student should determine whether the teacher remained in the same location.

> Step 2: The student either follows the teacher to the next activity or remains in the same area because the teacher did not move
>
> Ensure that the student has multiple opportunities to practice this skill. Over time, the switches should become less obvious (reduce and fade the within-stimulus prompts), the preference for initial activities should be increased (and preference for the second activity decreased), the time spent at each activity should be varied, and the distance between activities should be increased.

PHASE 2: Going with the flow: Phase 1 learning with a peer. The student learns to observe a peer and determine whether the peer has stayed or left the area using the same steps as described in Phase 1. Preferred peers should be involved in this phase (for development of peer preference, see the "Social Interest" program), so that there is intrinsic value to staying or following a peer during the flow of social play.

Again, within-stimulus prompts are best for this phase. Over time, the switches should become less obvious, the preference for initial activities should be increased (and preference for the second activity decreased), the time spent at each activity should be varied (longer periods at activities before switches), the distance between activities should be increased, and the peer group size and number of activities involved should be increased.

PHASE 3: To flow or not to flow: Choice making in group social play. The objective in this phase is to teach the student to decide whether to follow peers he or she was playing with, stay with the original activity, or switch to a new group involved in a different activity. This learning helps develop flexible choice making regarding play options that typically arise in free play social situations.

The following variables may be manipulated in Phase 3:

- Preference for activity
- Degree of completion of activity
- Level of satiation with activity
- Novelty of activity
- Preference for peers involved

Initially, situations should be set up in which the choices are clear (e.g., a preferred peer is moving from completed, nonpreferred activity to a highly novel and preferred activity; less preferred peers are moving from a highly preferred activity that was just begun; a less preferred peer stays with a completed activity when a new, preferred activity is initiated). External reinforcement is provided as necessary for "making the right choice." Over time, variables are altered to make the choices less clear (but still point to more or less "correct" choices), external reinforcers are faded (good outcomes are intrinsically and naturally reinforcing good choices), and work moves from orchestrated play arrangements to naturally occurring social play opportunities.

Vicarious Learning

Objectives

- Learn by observing the consequences experienced by others
- Increase contingency understanding
- Develop receptivity to a more natural means of managing behavior
- Increase social awareness and interest in others
- Increase reinforcement value of others
- Increase confidence in group situations

Prerequisites

- Basic contingency understanding
- Environmental awareness★
- Basic observational learning skills★
- Gestures★
- Basic social cue understanding
- Recall (intermediate phases)★
- Inferencing (later phases)

★See *A Work in Progress.*

Procedure

This program teaches a student what to do and—perhaps more importantly—what not to do in more generalized teaching environments. By observing the consequences experienced by peers, the student can learn to monitor and possibly adjust his or her own behavior without having to experience the consequences directly. Discrete Trial Teaching is the most effective instructional technique to promote this skill.

The appropriate behaviors targeted by this program are not skills in acquisition. Instead, they are established responses, either desired or undesired, depending on the setting or circumstances. For example, a student starting work immediately is praiseworthy when the activity is part of an established routine or the expectation is inherent. By comparison, starting work immediately when the task is new might be discouraged (an established behavior requiring corrective feedback), because the teacher may have specific instructions that the student should listen to before beginning. The student would need to better discriminate where and when to respond, based on environmental cues (the behavior exhibited and consequences experienced by others) rather than by habit or routine. These appropriate and inappropriate behaviors should be varied, because the goal of this program is establishing generalized vicarious learning, not altering specific behaviors.

For Phases 1 through 3, refer to the prompt continua following Phase 3. In each phase, work should move along the relevant prompt continua toward independent vicarious learning.

PHASE 1: The student behaves appropriately based on a positive consequence experienced by a peer. After watching a peer experience a positive consequence for a behavior (such as attending to a lesson, successfully following an instruction, or participating in an established classroom routine without being prompted), the student is provided with an opportunity to engage in the same or similar behavior. If the student engages in the desired behavior, then the same positive consequence should result. Prompts can be utilized to better promote attending and success. Have a systematic plan to fade those prompts so that the target behaviors eventually occur as independently as possible.

PHASE 2: The student changes inappropriate behavior when a peer experiences a positive consequence for refraining from inappropriate behavior. When the student engages in a mildly inappropriate behavior, within earshot, provide a peer with positive consequences for refraining from that behavior. Ensure that greater positive consequences result if, in addition, the peer is displaying an appropriate alternative behavior. If—based on hearing the consequence given to the peer—the student ceases the inappropriate behavior and/or engages in an appropriate alternative, then a positive consequence similar to the one received by the peer should result.

PHASE 3: The student refrains from inappropriate behavior after observing a peer receive corrective feedback. When a peer engages in an undesirable behavior during a specific stimulus situation (for example, a peer engages in self-stimulatory behavior during a pause in teaching) and receives corrective feedback, the student should be exposed to the same stimulus situation. If the student refrains from engaging in an undesirable behavior, provide reinforcement.

Phases 1–3 Prompt Continua

Immediacy of Student Opportunity Following Peer's Experience of Consequence

- Immediate
- Delayed

Proximity of Peer

- Close by student
- At a distance from student

(continued)

Phases 1–3 Prompt Continua

Conspicuousness of Consequence Experienced by Peer

- Exaggerated delivery
- Delivered in passing

Student's Preference for Positive Consequence

- Highly preferred
- Somewhat preferred

Nature of Discouraging Consequence Experienced by Peer

- Moderately discouraging
- Mildly discouraging

Peer Personality Attributes

- Highly familiar/preferred peer
- Unfamiliar/neutral peer

Behavior Similarities Between Child and Peer

- Identical
- Somewhat similar

PHASE 4: Develop skill generality. Situations like those described in Phases 1 through 3 are randomly and unpredictably presented.

PHASE 5: Increase environmental naturalness. The student changes behavior based on consequences experienced by peers in natural and incidentally occurring situations.

PHASE 6: Expanded vicarious learning. The student's behavior is based on consequences experienced by peers that the student heard about (or read about) but did not see. For example, a peer tells the student, "I got in trouble when I tried to open the emergency exit in the school auditorium." The student refrains from touching the emergency exit when next in the school auditorium.

Group Affiliation and Social Influence

Objectives

- Develop age-appropriate interests
- Increase awareness and knowledge about current popular culture
- Increase interest, desire, and comfort when relating to peers
- Strengthen susceptibility to peer influence and popular culture
- Increase peer acceptance

Prerequisites

- Social awareness
- Environmental awareness
- General knowledge and reasoning★
- Age-appropriate interest identification
- Social categories
- "Who do you choose?"
- Advanced conversation skills★

★See *A Work in Progress.*

Procedure

Phases 1 and 2 are designed to promote group affiliation. Phases 3 and 4 are designed to move some students beyond that affiliation such that they develop a measure of openness to peer, social, and cultural influences. All the phases within this program require advanced capabilities from the student. For some students, only the first two phases are applicable. For others, the third and fourth phases may lead to development of only limited capabilities. Rather than working toward a goal of skill mastery, Phases 3 and 4 focus on enhancing the student's susceptibility—to whatever extent possible—to subtle social forces. This objective is aimed primarily at secondary school–aged students (ages 13 through 18). However, some phase components (particularly the group process material) are applicable to students of preschool age and older.

PHASE 1: Building group affiliation. The student creates an "interest list" based on individual preferences. Activities relating to contemporary culture should be considered when creating this list, as group activities are likely to be tied into the larger youth culture.

Help the student gather information about—and begin participating in—a range of activities relating to those interests. Some students may require Teaching Interactions to develop meaningful rationales for participation in this program. Although acquiring inherent motivation through participation in the activity is important, the student may initially require supplemental reinforcement to better develop interest, enjoyment, and ultimately desire to engage in the activity. Keep the student's parents informed; their permission may be necessary based on the "interest list" and activities the student may choose (for example, using the Internet).

As interests develop, have the student participate in social groups, activities, and clubs (e.g., bands, videogame clubs, anime groups, lunch comedy sessions, action card groups). Be sure these activities and clubs are directly tied to the student's chosen interests.

The following example assumes that the student voices an interest in popular music:

Interest: Popular Music

Related Potential Social Activities

- Listening to CDs
- Watch music videos
- Listen to the radio
- Shop at music stores
- Learn to play an instrument
- Visit band websites
- Select a topic for class
- Presentations

- Concerts
- Music-related videogames
- Garage bands
- Fan clubs
- School dances
- Band chat rooms
- Air band contests
- Karaoke parties

It may be necessary to create social groups or clubs in the community or school settings that cater to the student's interest, for two reasons. First, such groups or clubs may not exist. Second, a teacher or therapist may help create these groups and clubs (for example, as a faculty sponsor) to allow for embedded, systematic teaching to occur.

PHASE 2: Group affiliation: Evaluation and review. After participating in both individual and group activities based on the chosen interest, the student evaluates his or her enjoyment level and interest strength. The student determines whether to participate in specific activities and whether to explore other related activities. For example, if the student remains highly interested in popular music but the school band was not enjoyable, then generate a list of other activities related to popular music that the student can try.

PHASE 3: Building a "group effect." This phase is designed to promote the child's openness and responsivity to group effects. *Group effects* are subtle phenomena in which the simultaneous activity or collective response of the group produces an enhanced impact on the experience (e.g., cheering during a concert, collective silliness in a class, one-upmanship comments to the camp counselor, the rise in spontaneous chatter when the teacher leaves a middle school class, laughter in a crowded theater—as compared to the laughter when watching the same comedy alone). Such group effects tend to increase the richness, momentum, or intensity of the experience and the responses. The goal of this step is to promote susceptibility to this effect in the child. Responsivity to such effects is a usual occurrence for typically developing children. It is a way that they connect with, contribute to, and—perhaps most importantly—gain and learn from a group and its process.

During the group and shared activities established in Phase 1, orchestrate group effect opportunities. For example, schedule activities with a high likelihood of group effect occurrence, or coach group members to create a group effect process. The following strategies may be used:

- Identify areas of greater activity interest, as greater initial interest should increase the likelihood of the student responding to and participating in the group effect.
- Initially, create "group effect temptations" (motivating operations). Emphasize the group process's reinforcement value. A typical way of doing so is to increase the "fun factor" of the collective group action. Here are some specific group effect temptation ideas:
  - The group simultaneously stomps and claps, gradually increasing the pace and volume.
  - Make a "buzz-o-meter" or "silly-o-meter"—depending on the children's age—and use it to gauge the noise or activity level of boys versus girls.
  - For younger students, hold a star on a stick or fishing pole above the group; each group tries to catch the star.
  - For older students, engage in "snaps." Students or the class as a whole collectively and repeatedly snap fingers when someone achieves a success or does something praiseworthy.
- If prompting is necessary, use within-stimulus prompts. Instruct peers to heighten the intensity of the group effect to draw the student's attention and participation (e.g., the group cheers louder; the group dramatically goes off-task; over-the-top silliness).
- Set up a hierarchy ranging from those group effects that the student is most likely to notice and respond to those group effects that the student is least likely to respond to. Expose the student to the hierarchy systematically. For example, move from a group effect with an auditory component only, such as peers chanting loudly, "Winter break is coming! Winter break is coming!", to a more subtle group effect, such as everyone sequentially faking a cough.
- External reinforcement for instances of student responsiveness to the group effect may be initially necessary. What is reinforced, however, is not the quality of the performance of the specific action or behavior that was exhibited within the group effect episode, but rather the *responsivity* to the group effect (e.g., "Hey, look at you joining in!"). Such external and enhanced reinforcement should be faded over time as the independent susceptibility to the group effect increases.
- Vary group effect opportunities, randomizing their occurrence throughout the day or week. The objective is to create a generalized susceptibility across many forms of the group effect.

PHASE 4: Building social influence. As the student becomes more receptive to group effect activities, the next step is to expand the student's susceptibility to peer and social influences within the current youth culture.

The student displays "susceptibility to social influence" by learning new information and response styles (both verbal and nonverbal) and by developing new interests, desires, or pursuits due to exposure to the peer group and youth culture. This development occurs without explicit direction and is based solely on the exposure. The objective is a more generalized social learning, which is both incidental and fairly broad (across instances and types of exposure). The child is affected by the exposure in a particular way—for example, he or she develops a youth culture interest, wants something, picks up a catch phrase, or adopts an affectation. Again, the goal is a generalized and incidental susceptibility to the peer culture. Be careful to monitor this growth, as would be the case with any teenager swayed by peers and popular culture.

Possible avenues of exposure and influence include the following:

- Peer groups and clubs as described in Phase 1
- Music
- Television
- Magazines
- Theater
- Movies
- Websites
- Texting
- Online social networking

The following strategies are recommended:

- Exposure to social or group occurrences or phenomena containing established interests should facilitate the susceptibility to the social influence process.
- As during Phase 3, create "susceptibility to social influence temptations" by promoting receptivity to incidental youth culture exposure.
  - Emphasize and enhance the reinforcement value of the specific youth culture content.
  - Present youth culture material relating to formerly established interests and activities (from Phases 1 and 2) during the exposure of Phase 4. Presenting youth culture content in an attractive, fun, and novel manner further enhances its reinforcement value. Some specific "susceptibility to social influence temptations" ideas are suggested here:
    - During Anime Club, peers repeatedly and excitedly talk about a new DVD.
    - The band members wear a new T-shirt with the band's name on it; extra shirts are left lying around.
    - Peers in the Action Video Game Group communally use the same phrase that a character in a videogame uses.

Each scenario potentially increases the reinforcement value of the youth culture content and, therefore, increases the probability of student susceptibility to the content.

- To promote incidental and spontaneous responses, prompting strategies similar to those described in Phase 3 can be used. These prompts should make the youth culture content (e.g., styles, mannerisms and affectations, music groups, celebrities and icons, youth consumer products) more appealing. As the skill is developed, fade these prompts. Over time, the content should be presented more incidentally and subtly.

- Initially, the student may be asked to immediately recall something witnessed, gained, learned, or desired after the exposure. If such a practice is used at all, have a systematic plan to fade this highly intrusive prompt, as it might interfere with spontaneous and incidental nature of the influence process.

- When the student demonstrates any signs of the influence produced by exposure to the youth culture, use external reinforcement or social praise as necessary. These instances can include evidence of new interests, the adoption of a style or mannerism, the desire for an item, or the use of specific slang. Remember: what is reinforced is not what has been specifically acquired (such as new clothing being worn). Rather, reinforcement should occur because *something* has been acquired due to the social influence process. Praise might take the following form: "I saw you skateboarding. You learned to do that from your friends, didn't you? Awesome!" Such external reinforcement, if used, should be faded as quickly as possible, as the independent susceptibility to social forces increases.

- Peer and social influence situations and opportunities need to be varied and rotated consistently. The idea is not to build one specific type or form of response to social influence, but rather to develop generalized susceptibility across many avenues and episodes of youth culture exposure.

SOCIAL RELATEDNESS

Tolerating the Presence
and Proximity of Peers

Objectives

- Reduce student isolation and withdrawal
- Work on areas necessary for all other social programming
- Create opportunities for further social skills instruction

Prerequisites

- Sitting and staying in a seat or an area for at least brief periods★
- Basic compliance★
- Understanding of contingency★

★See *A Work in Progress.*

Procedure

For this program, gradual, systematic programming is essential for progress and comprehensive change. Although reinforcement may be used for participation and curricular progression, the following is essentially a respondent learning-oriented (desensitization) program. With patience and systematic teaching, the student should not only be able to spend extended periods in proximity of peers, but also be available for further social teaching.

PHASE 1: Develop a protocol for producing a calm state in the student. This could include listening to music, deep breathing, tensing and releasing muscles, or any process or combination of techniques producing a relaxed condition, without adversely affecting attention and responsiveness. Every individual is different regarding what might produce a truly calmative state.

PHASE 2: Set the stage. Utilize the relaxation protocol in a tranquil and comfortable setting until it consistently produces a calming affect.

PHASE 3: Develop a hierarchy. Create a ranking of social proximity arrangements and circumstances producing discomfort and intolerance (from least to most). For example, at the initial level, this could involve a quiet, nonthreatening peer who is standing 10 feet away for 5 seconds. Steps up the hierarchy increase all the relevant dimensions until the situations include the most stressful and provocative elements identified—for example, the student sitting between two peers, shoulder to shoulder, at a table with three more peers, engaged in a loud and active task in a noisy classroom for a half hour.

PHASE 4: Introduce the hierarchy systematically and gradually. While the student is in the relaxed state, introduce the first hierarchical situations—that is, those least intolerant to the student. If the student displays discomfort or stress, immediately discontinue the scenario (and develop even less provocative early steps in the hierarchy). However, if the student maintains calm in the presence of the step, repeat it until calm occurs with consistency (approximately three times in a row). At that point, move forward to the next step. This process is continued through each step, either moving forward or backward (and then forward again) based on the effect on the student.

Further Steps

Ultimately, the student should move to tolerating a range of typically encountered and naturally occurring peer presence arrangements so further social programming and instruction can proceed.

Joint Attention II

Objectives

- Increase social referencing
- Increase awareness of social environment
- Increase social connection and responsivity
- Begin building and recognizing shared experience

Prerequisites

- Joint attention★
- Basic receptive labeling★
- Basic receptive instructions★

★See A Work in Progress.

Procedure

There are two types of joint attention typically referred to in the literature: having others follow your actions or gaze (e.g., checking to see a parent is watching you or what you are observing) and spontaneously orienting oneself to the object of the other's gaze (looking up to see what everyone else is gazing at). These critical skills are fundamental to ongoing social learning and awareness. They are also early indicators of social connection.

PHASE 1: Build desire. The focus of this phase is to build the student's desire for his or her gaze to be noticed and joined by another. This can be addressed through the following strategy.

- Place motivating and intrinsically intriguing items close to the student (prior to this phase, developing a strong, individualized motivator/reinforcement inventory would be necessary). These items should, sometime after placement, catch the student's attention. This goal can be accomplished by the item suddenly producing sound, movement, or other attention-getting signals. To promote the likelihood of catching someone else's look or attention after something interesting has occurred, the teacher should be sufficiently close to the item, within the student's field of vision, when the student is orienting toward the item. The teacher should be focused on neither the item nor the student. The following progression of steps should be followed:
  - As soon as the student orients to the item, the teacher should quickly orient to the child.
  - The teacher should immediately follow the student's gaze to the item. This should be done overtly, graphically, and dramatically (a within-stimulus prompt), and should be paired with a comment such as "What are you looking at? . . . Oh, cool!"; "I see it now, too!"; "What do you see? . . . Ahh, let me get it for you."
  - The student is then reinforced, preferably with the item.

218

- Timing is critical in this procedure: The teacher should not look at the student or the item before the student does or wait too long to look after the student does. Over time, as the skill develops, prompts can be faded and all the instructional elements can be extended and naturalized (e.g., teacher proximity can change).

- The teacher should provide a closed-ended task to the student.
  - When the task is completed and the student is clearly looking at the finished product, the teacher should quickly follow the student's gaze and make statements similar to the preceding examples. Further phrases, based on the task, may include statements such as "What do you see? . . . Oh, you're done!" or "You did it!"
  - The student should then be reinforced.
  - Timing is critical to establishing the contingency.

- If the student has expressive capacity, teach him or her phrases designed to direct others to follow his or her gaze in situations like those described previously.
  - Phrases such as "Look!" and "You have to see this!" can be taught by using prompts (e.g., verbal imitation prompts) while the student is orienting toward the items, achievements, or other phenomena.
  - Prompts need to be faded as quickly as possible.
  - The teacher should, upon the student's verbal request, dramatically follow the student's gaze, verbally acknowledge the item or phenomenon, and reinforce the invitation for shared attention, as described previously.

PHASE 2: Extend the skills. With the joint attending contingencies established, the teacher should require persistence on the part of the child before gazing at the item or product and then delivering reinforcement. For example, the child must look at the item or product and then look at the teacher and return his or her gaze to the item before receiving reinforcement; alternatively or concomitantly, the student must gesture toward the item or vocally attempt to have the teacher reference the item before teacher attention is provided and reinforcement is provided. In such ways, the child's desire and effort to gain joint attention are magnified.

PHASE 3: Do you see what I see? This and the following phases teach the student to follow someone else's gaze. This phase involves the following procedure:
- Provide the student with a basic receptive labeling task at a table with two novel items.
  - The teacher should be seated across from the student.
  - The only prompt assisting the student in identifying the correct requested item is a direct gaze from the teacher to the item.
  - A prerequisite, added prompt may be necessary. This prompt could take the form of a slight head incline toward the correct item.
  - In time, and with the introduction of many items, head orientation should be less and less prominent and only eye gaze should be utilized to direct the student toward the correct answer.

- Although reinforcement may be provided for correct identification of item, the use of gaze for arriving at that correct answer is actually reinforced because the "prompt" is not faded in these trials.

PHASE 4: Reinforcement acquisition results from following gaze. This phase involves the following procedure:

- Engage the student in a one-to-one teaching task at a table.
  - This activity should be near mastery, ensuring a high rate of success and subsequent reinforcement availability.
- Instead of the student directly receiving a tangible reinforcer at the end of a successful trial, the teacher should say, "Where is the (*name of reinforcing object*)?"
- The teacher should then use his or her gaze to indicate the reinforcer's location.
- Once the student correctly follows the teacher's gaze, the reinforcer is made accessible.
  - If necessary, the teacher may prompt with head orientation accompanying the gaze, then fade to eye gaze only.
- Over time, the reinforcer location question should be faded and only gaze should be used to indicate the location of the reinforcer.
- Similarly, over time, the reinforcer should be located at a distance from the working area.

PHASE 5: Begin generalization work. The teaching is gradually moved from a table with the correct stimulus item or reinforcer (respective to the previously mentioned phases) to a distance in the environment.

PHASE 6: Teach multiple reasons to follow someone's gaze. Gaze is utilized not only to indicate the correct answer or the location of reinforcers at the end of trials, but also to identify the location of preferred items at other times, the placement of items necessary to complete effort, and, outside of trial effort, the occurrence of unusual, compelling, and interesting phenomena or activities.

Peer Social Interest and Engagement

Objectives*

- Increase environmental awareness
- Increase attention to others
- Increase the reinforcement value of peers
- Increase interest in and desire to be around for peers
- Increase overall social motivation
- Enhance the quality of peer interaction
- Develop prerequisites for group peer experiences
- Build requisites for relationship development

*Along with work directed at developing social interest and engagement, serious effort must be directed at simultaneously building social competencies. Without social skills to promote social success, social engagement and interest may dissipate or the circumstance will result in a profound and painful sense of yearning, unfulfilled desire, and failure.

Prerequisites

- Tolerating the presence and proximity of peers
- Basic environmental awareness†
- Basic and intermediate observational awareness†
- Observational learning skills†

*See *A Work in Progress.*

Procedure

By developing and presenting a wide variety of situations and activities, this program focuses on increasing the motivating operations associated with peers and increasing their reinforcement value to the student. Movement from Phase 1 to Phase 2 represents shaping to a more complete and complex version of the skill. Phase 3 represents a generalized skill expansion. All phases will require the assistance and support of peers.

PHASE 1: Building interest and engagement. Set up situations and activities enhancing the interest and reinforcement value of specific peer(s). Situations could include the following scenarios:

- The peer selects or plays with a preferred object or toy
- The peer has, hides, or finds a needed item (e.g., a straw for a juice box)
- The peer provides reinforcement (end-of-trial reinforcement)

- The peer provides necessary prompts
- The peer serves as an observational model (e.g., the peer shows a novel way to use a preferred toy; the peer provides a nonverbal observational prompt for a receptive labeling task)
- The peer engages in extended novel activity
- The peer rescues the student—that is, the peer's arrival (and subsequent interaction/activity with the peer) results in the stoppage of and escape from a nonpreferred activity
- The peer builds anticipation for an activity or outcome (excitedly saying, "This is going to be great" or "I can't wait for recess!"; after doing something fun two times, the peer pauses before the third repetition, building anticipatory excitement)
- The student engages in competitive or cooperative activities with the peer (e.g., winning a three-legged race)
- Peer participation enhances play activity (e.g., the peer can help the merry-go-round spin faster; the peer and the student both stepping on the pedal makes the rocket shoot higher)
- Activities are selected that require two people to fully enjoy them, so the student must engage with a peer to participate (e.g., teeter-totter, wagon pull, blanket swing, "Zoomball")
- Several highly preferred activities are kept off-limits unless the student has a peer to play with (e.g., watching a specific video, making cookies, throwing water balloons)

Each of these situations provides an opportunity for increasing the peer reinforcement value. Each also creates the opportunity for the occurrence and subsequent reinforcement of socially engaged behavior. Although the situations all contain intrinsic reinforcement, for some students, providing additional extrinsic reinforcement may be necessary. The idea is not only to create opportunities, but also to reinforce the engaged and socially interested responses that the opportunities present.

Instances of engaged and interested student behavior in response to peers warranting reinforcement include the following examples:

- Extended tracking
- Approach or gravitation toward a peer
- Anticipatory response
- Attention and contact seeking
- Extended proximity or interaction
- Joint attention
- Preference

PHASE 2: Enhanced interest and engagement. This phase, through shaping, is designed to build and deepen the quality (including the affective component) of engagement and interest during peer interaction. Instances of increased engagement are reinforced differentially. As in Phase 1, situations and activities increasing the opportunity for more engaged interaction are artificial and contrived. Increased degrees of social engagement are differentially reinforced with feedback and higher-level tangibles as appropriate.

Over time, efforts should move from external to natural and intrinsic reinforcement and from work in contrived scenarios to more naturalistic situations. Examples of enhanced levels of peer social engagement include the following:

- More enthusiastic participation in activities
- More consistent social referencing (joint attention)
- More consistent, spontaneous, or varied imitation of the peer
- Amplified competitive drive
- Displays of enhanced anticipation
- Excitement with the appearance of the peer
- Responses that indicate disappointment with the absence of the peer
- Active and preferential selection of, or request for, specific peer(s)
- Approval seeking
- Disapproval avoidance

PHASE 3: Groups of peers. In this phase, work moves from developing interest in specific peers(s) to developing interest in groups of peers. The goal is to promote greater interest and engaged participation in group social experiences. As in Phases 1 and 2, efforts are initially directed at developing the reinforcement value of group experiences and creating opportunities for interested and engaged responding through contrived experiences. Pre-teaching of group activities may be necessary. Setup situations could include the following scenarios:

- The group is involved in preferred activities or is using favored items
- The group includes preferred peer(s) (as established in earlier phases)
- The group is engaged in novel, eye-catching, or mysterious activities
- The group is involved in high-energy and exciting interactive, cooperative, or competitive activity (e.g., a relay race)

As with earlier phases, efforts are directed at reinforcing the interest and engaged participation created by the setup activities and opportunities. Interested and engaged behaviors to reinforce in this phase may include these examples:

- Tracking of group activity
- Curiosity about group goings-on
- Gravitation toward the group
- Engaged participation in the group

Finally, as in Phase 2, reinforcement fades to naturally occurring consequences and effort is moved from contrived scenarios to naturally occurring situations and circumstances.

Being a Good Friend

Objectives

- Develop competencies that enhance true friendships
- Develop awareness of and connection to others
- Develop a host of prosocial interactional and relationship skills
- Enhance functioning in the interactional and social world

Prerequisites

- Acquisition of advanced social awareness skills
- Acquisition of intermediate to advanced social communication skills★
- Acquisition of intermediate to advanced social interaction skills
- Basic inferences
- Acquisition of advanced social learning skills

★See *A Work in Progress.*

Procedure

The following programmatic elements are taught using discrimination training, Teaching Interactions, and—perhaps most critically—generalization programming to move ultimately authentic competencies into actually occurring relationships and naturally occurring situations. These elements contained in this program do not represent an exhaustive list, and variations certainly exist in what constitutes the elements of a good friend as well as good friendship. Nevertheless, the presence of at least a portion of the elements offered could accurately be characterized as the minimum.

ELEMENT 1: Actively listening to and watching other people. The focus here is on being aware of comprehending the communications and actions of the peer (as opposed to being largely egocentrically or self-stimulation focused).

- In a conversation or discussion with a peer (both before and after you speak):
  - Pause and try not to think about what you have said or are going to say.
  - Concentrate on what the peer is saying and doing.
  - Repeat to yourself what you heard and saw.
  - Check with yourself if you understand what you heard and saw.
    - If you do not understand, ask a clarifying question such as "I don't understand what you mean."
    - If you do understand, continue the conversation.
  - Other conversational elements can be added in time.

ELEMENT 2: Knowing the other's likes and dislikes. This element involves the child learning to focus on those statements, choices, and actions offered by a peer that provide information or clues about the other person's likes and dislikes (e.g. items, activities, foods, entertainments). For children who have developed the ability to infer, work would focus on generating a sense of likes and dislikes inferentially. Effort would begin in structured simulations and progress to natural circumstances.

ELEMENT 3: Friendship communication. Work in this area comprises a series of discrimination training sessions on the forms, types, and components of friendship communication (e.g., honest talk, sharing of intimacies, white lies to spare someone's feelings or preserve a secret) that are shared by true friends. Generalization to actual friendship conversation (or to work directed at developing true friendships) would follow. Some content examples are provided here:

- Openness
  - Degrees of openness
  - When to be open
  - When openness can actually be hurtful

- Giving advice
  - When to give (Is it solicited?)
  - In which areas?
  - When a suggestion is more than a suggestion
  - Politely refusing

- White lies
  - White lies versus plain old lying
  - When are white lies okay?

- Personal information
  - Why?
  - What can and should not be shared
  - When to give
  - Styles and manner of sharing

ELEMENT 4: Reciprocity, one-sidedness, and exploitation. Discrimination training and skill instruction are directed at the components of mutuality and equity that constitute true friendships and the actions and gestures that maintain relationship reciprocity. Such teaching includes such features as the following:

- Give and take
- Mutual favors
- Parity of effort and actions
- Matched support

ELEMENT 5: Politeness, respect, and appreciation. Effort is directed at discrimination training and teaching of skills related to the respectful treatment of a friend. As an example, the following is a task analysis to be used in the skill instruction of appreciation:

Following a positive act by a friend

- Evaluate the level of the act:
  - A small act or gesture
  - A big act or gesture
- If it was a small act:
  - Make a statement (with positive and enthusiastic tone) of thanks (e.g., "Really appreciate it")
  - Make a statement of possible reciprocation (e.g., "I will do the same for you some day")
- If it was a large act:
  - Make an enthusiastic statement of appreciation as above
  - Perform a gesture of appreciation (e.g., send the person a "thank you" message; draw a special "thank you" picture; buy some candy or a small gift)

ELEMENT 6: Common interests, shared activities. For information on how to approach the teaching of this area, see the program "Group Affiliation and Social Influence."

ELEMENT 7: Sharing and shared experience. For information on how to approach the teaching of this area, see the program "Sharing."

ELEMENT 8: Anticipating the other's feelings, preferences, and actions. For information on how to approach the teaching of this area, see the program "Perspective Taking."

ELEMENT 9: Discussing and constructive arguing. For information on how to approach the teaching of this area, see the program "Arguing, Discussing, Persuading, and Letting Go."

ELEMENT 10: Empathy and caring. For information on how to approach the teaching of these higher-order areas, see the program "Caring Responses and Empathy."

ELEMENT 11: Compromise and putting a friend first. The emphasis of this element is on the situations in which it is appropriate to put the other person first and how to do that. Compromise is also covered. Training in what is important and unimportant as well as in flexibility is a prerequisite. The following is an example task analysis on "putting a friend first."

- You and a friend cannot agree on a decision or choice:
  - Think about what you want.
  - Think about what the friend wants.

- Weigh and compare the importance of what you want against what the friend wants.
- Add other relevant factors to the balance. For example:
  - Who last got their way
  - How important the friend is to you
  - How much you want or need to show appreciation to the friend
- Weigh and compare all the factors for and against giving up what you want and putting your friend first.
- If you struggle to give up what you want:
  - Try compromising (task analysis follows later in this program).
  - Alternatively, end the discussion in a polite way.
- If the factors for giving up what you want are greater, then put your friend's needs first.

The following is an example task analysis on "compromising."

- You and a friend cannot agree on a decision or choice:
  - Think about the part of your side (of the issue or disagreement) that is the most important and the part you can give up.
  - Ask if your friend can do the same.
  - If the friend will not:
    - Do what friend wants (see the program "Assertion" from *A Work in Progress*).
    - Alternatively, end the discussion politely (e.g., "Sorry we couldn't work out"; "Maybe next time").
  - If the friend will:
    - Ask yourself if "nothing at all" is better than just the part you would get from the compromise.
    - If "nothing at all" is better, then end the discussion politely.
    - If "just the part" is better, then ask the friend what his or her "important" and "give-up" parts are.
    - Discuss if your important part and the friend's important part can happen compatibly (simultaneously, in alternating fashion, and so on).
  - If this can occur, then end the discussion and move on (compromise is reached).
  - If this cannot occur, then try the preceding steps again (to try to reduce each person's "important" parts and increase the number of "give-up" parts, thereby increasing the chance for compromise/agreement).
  - If the second attempt does not work, end the exchange politely.
  - If the second attempt works, then end the discussion and move on (compromise is reached).

ELEMENT 12: Standing up for yourself. For information on how to approach the teaching of this area, see the program "Assertion" in *A Work in Progress*.

ELEMENT 13: Being supportive and getting support. This element includes such abilities as just being present when a friend is upset, enjoying a friend's accomplishment (see the "Sharing" program), letting a friend vent, generally being there for a friend, and letting someone be there for the student.

Targets typically involve using affective statements and performing a series of steps or actions, and teaching begins with structured role-plays. Work is directed at gradually moving this teaching to authentic situations. An example of a task analysis for "showing concern and offering support" follows:

- If a friend appears upset:
  - Approach the friend.
    - The student stands as close to the friend as the established personal space allows (typically around 3 feet).
  - Face the friend.
    - The student directly faces the friend for the entire duration of the interaction.
  - The student makes appropriate eye contact throughout the interaction.
    - This includes typical levels of eye contact (e.g., looking away or down, then reorienting to the friend).
  - The student has a facial expression congruous with the mood of the exchange (e.g., interested, concerned, caring, active listening).
  - Voice volume is soft, with a respectful tone used.
  - The student retains a relaxed body and posture.
    - The student stands (or sits up straight, depending on the environment and the friend's physical positioning) without any tenseness.
    - The student's body leans slightly toward the friend.
  - The student asks a general question demonstrating concern (e.g., "Are you okay?" or "Is everything alright?").
  - If the friend does not answer or states that he or she does not require help or support, the student waits a short while (approximately 10 to 15 seconds) and then provides an offer of future help (e.g., "If you need anything, let me know").
  - If the friend does answer and indicates the need for help, then the student asks a more specific question regarding the friend's response to the general question (e.g., "What's the matter?").
  - Whether or not the friend provides more information, the student then asks the friend if anything can be done to make the situation better.
  - If the peer says "yes":
    - The student does what is asked if appropriate and doable.

- If the friend says "no":
  - The student simply acknowledges that response with a comment or a gesture (e.g., "Okay" or a nod).
- The student makes a follow-up statement, such as "Let me know if there is anything [or "anything else" if help has been provided] I can do."
- The student again provides the friend with a gesture of caring, such as a pat on the back or a head nod.

Caring Responses and Empathy

Objectives

- Increase the quality of social relationships
- Share emotional experiences with others
- Respond to the emotional needs of others
- Increase social awareness, connectedness, and sensitivity

Prerequisites

- Emotions★
- Cause and effect★
- Inferences
- Perspective taking

★See *A Work in Progress.*

Procedure

Stage 1 develops the student's awareness and understanding of others' emotional needs. Further, the student learns appropriate, caring responses to others' emotional presentations. This stage can be run individually or in a small group. Small groups allow for opportunities for immediate practice with peers.

Stage 2 increases the student's ability to experience and share authentic, empathic emotional responses. The goal for this stage is not merely the performance of empathic behaviors or provision of empathic statements, but rather the development of authentic empathic emotional responses in the individual. The aim is to build the student's capacity for true empathy.

While Stage 2 primarily teaches emotional responsiveness by using respondent learning-oriented methodologies, the student may require more overt reinforcement for participating in the activity. Stages 1 and 2 can be taught simultaneously.

Stage 1

PHASE 1: Emotional cause and effect. The student learns to identify situations likely to create emotional arousal, the likely resultant emotional state, and the rationale for why a particular emotional outcome occurred. Examples include:

- "The boy is happy because his team is going to win."
- "She's going to be upset because she fell off her bike."
- "He may become jealous because his classmate won a prize."

The student learns to predict potential emotional outcomes based on situational precursors. The student also learns to explain possible causes or antecedent circumstances based on presentations of scenarios depicting emotional outcomes (with some clues of precursors provided).

Strategy 1: Watch videotapes of known people or movie clips.

Strategy 2: Role-play.

Strategy 3: Observe real-life events.

PHASE 2: Caring responses to others' emotions. The student identifies and describes appropriate ways to respond to situations in which another person is experiencing a state of emotional arousal. Considerations include the following issues:

- Is an immediate response appropriate or possible?
  - If not, student further determines when the response should appropriately occur.
- The student identifies multiple responses:
  - What he or she can do to make the other person feel better
  - How he or she can demonstrate a shared understanding ("That's happened to me")
  - How he or she can show support (giving a smile or comforting gesture; asking the person, "What can I do to help?")

Discussions of such mitigating factors as gender differences, cultural concerns, age appropriateness, "saving face" concerns, issues of privacy, and timing may be helpful during this phase.

Examples of "caring response" exercises follow:

- Teacher: "What should you do if you see a classmate fall down? "
  - Possible student responses: Ask if he's okay; get an adult.
- Teacher: "What happens if your brother can't find his homework and seems worried about it?"
  - Possible student responses: Say, "Can I help you look for it?"; offer to help him do the work again.
- Teacher: "Your friend just won a game."
  - Possible student responses: Give him a high five; say, "Congratulations!"
- Teacher: "Your buddy gets scolded by the teacher."
  - Possible student responses: Check in with him after class; tell him, "The same thing happened to me, but I turned it around; the teacher loves me now."

Step 1: Discussion of issues and relevant considerations

Step 2: Discrimination training

Watch videotapes and/or view stories and pictorial representations. The student determines whether a response shows caring. If not, the student should describe an alternative response. If a caring response is shown, the student could convey why it is representative of caring and describe additional appropriate responses.

Step 3: Role-play appropriate responses to scenarios involving others' emotional arousal

Work should specifically involve scenarios the student typically encounters during the day, including particularly challenging situations (e.g., sibling issues, when someone's upset occurs while the student is occupied). Switching roles during these role-plays allows the student to experience both the giving and the receiving of social support and understanding.

Sometimes an appropriate response to an emotional situation will result in an inappropriate response from the recipient. It may be helpful to address these types of situations with more advanced students with role-plays. For example, someone might not be receptive to you asking if the person is okay when he or she is feeling very embarrassed. In such a case, the student learns "Just because she snaps at you, it does not mean that you did not do the right thing."

PHASE 3: Scheduled presentations: Stopping and identifying. Present the student with situations throughout the day, requiring a response to another's emotional state. In this phase, the student learns to stop an activity, orient, and identify which situation has occurred. For example:

- The teacher pretends to slip down a few steps on the stairs and drops his or her books.
- After person 1 is working on a building project for some time, person 2 comes over and crushes person 1's structure.
- After trying and trying to figure something out, a peer becomes frustrated, pushes his or her seat back, and says he or she needs a break from the assignment.

Over time, situations should be presented when the student is increasingly preoccupied (e.g., engaged in increasingly preferred activities, near completion of an involving task). Further, with time, the unpredictability and subtlety of presentation should be increased. Situations involving a variety of individuals and emotional states should be included.

PHASE 4: Scheduled presentations: Caring responses. Again, present the student with situations throughout the day, requiring a response to another's emotional state. In this phase, after stopping, orienting, and identifying, the student engages in an appropriate response (covered in Phase 2) to the person.

As in the previous phase, over time, challenges to responding, unpredictability, and subtlety should be increased as pertinent for the presentation of situations. In addition to recognizing (and reinforcing as indicated) the appropriate and caring responses of the student, acknowledgment of the absence of inappropriate responses (e.g., laughing at the person, lengthy staring at someone who is upset, talking to someone who wants to be left alone) is also often instructionally appropriate.

Stage 2

PHASE 1: Empathic response: Self. This step and the following steps require sufficient video footage of the student and others. The student watches videos of himself or herself in situations that, when they occurred, evoked various emotional responses from the student. The goal of this phase is for the presentation to evoke the same emotional response the student experienced when the event actually occurred. At this point, however, the emotional response is occurring "at a distance"—that is, not at the same moment as the occurrence of the event and in response to "someone else" (really the student himself or herself, but with the small amount of detachment the video brings). Be sure to include both positive and negative emotional experiences (often we start with positive and move to more challenging experiences). Some examples include:

- Receiving an award
- Mild misfortunes (e.g., gum in hair, skinned knee)
- Acting in a play
- Getting hit with a ball and being laughed at
- Going to the amusement park

If the video does not evoke the emotional response, the student may need to watch events that have occurred more recently (even, for example, watching a video immediately after the occurrence of an event) or that have had a more significant impact. The alternative method described at the end of this program might also be tried.

PHASE 2: Empathic response: Others. With successful evocation of emotion in Phase 1, the student watches videos of people in his or her life to whom the student is close. The aim is for the video to evoke in the student a fitting emotional response to someone at a greater distance than in the previous phase—this time, truly "someone else." Include both positive and negative emotional experiences for the student to watch.

Over time, videos of others (e.g., favorite characters, sports figures, and celebrities in addition to friends and family members) are included. Work should proceed in hierarchical fashion; in other words, it should start with those persons most important to the student and move outward from there. Empathic response to those others who do not matter to the student should not be required.

If the student is not experiencing an emotional response to the video, it may be necessary to show video clips of the student experiencing emotional states immediately before showing a clip of others. It may also be important for the video clips of others to closely match the experiences in the video clips of the student. The alternative method described at the end of this program might also be tried.

PHASE 3: Empathic response: In vivo. With gains in Phase 2, over time, sessions should be moved to observation of (and eventually include participation in) in vivo situations that should be evocative of empathic responses. Initially, efforts should involve those persons who are closest to the student, but eventually move to others of some significance from there. Over time, effort should involve less orchestration and movement to monitoring empathic responses in naturally occurring circumstances.

Alternative Method for Stage 2, Phases 1 and 2: Guided Imagery

For some students, the technique described in this section may serve as an alternative means to progressively evoke empathic emotional responses and build empathic capacity.

Have the student relax with eyes closed and listen to a story or event being told. Initially, the story describes an experience the student actually had. The student should think about what was felt at the time. The aim is to evoke the same emotional response experienced at the time of event. Do not move on to further steps until this response is achieved. As described in Phases 1 and 2, start with positive images. As the student gains mastery of this step, the events and stories should be gradually and systematically expanded to include situations that could happen to the student and did and could happen to other persons. For example:

- "Remember when you won the spelling bee? When you spelled the last word correctly, everyone cheered and you jumped up and down. You had the biggest smile. Remember how that felt? Oh, I see you are smiling!"
- "Remember that day at school you were playing handball at recess? Some boy told you that you were out, but you didn't agree with him. You got pretty mad and started crying and tried to explain he was wrong. Some of the other kids starting laughing and told you to just get back at the end of line. Let's talk about how you are feeling as I am describing what happened to you."

Initially this exercise can be done with a visual "feelings chart." The student can use the chart to help develop a wider repertoire of emotional descriptors. The general objective is for the student to experience connected, congruous, empathic emotional responses. With success, work progresses to Stage 2, Phase 3.

References

1. Ali, S., & Frederickson, N. (2006). Investigating the evidence base of social stories *Educational Psychology in Practice, 22*(4), 355–377.

2. American Psychiatric Association. (1994). *Diagnostic and statistical manual of mental disorders* (4th ed.). Washington, DC: Author.

3. American Psychiatric Association. (2000). *Diagnostic and statistical manual of mental disorders* (4th ed., test rev.). Washington, DC: Author.

4. Aron, A., Melinat, E., Aron, E. N., Vallone, R. D., & Bator, R. J. (1997). The experimental generation of interpersonal closeness: A procedure and some preliminary findings. *Personality & Social Psychology Bulletin, 23,* 363–377.

5. Baron-Cohen, S. (1989). The autistic child's theory of mind: A case of specific developmental delay. *Journal of Child Psychology and Psychiatry, 30*(2), 81– 97.

6. Baron-Cohen, S. (1995). *Mindblindness: An essay on autism and theory of mind.* Cambridge, MA: MIT Press.

7. Baron-Cohen, S., Allen, J., & Gillberg, C. (1992). Can autism be detected at 18 months? The needle in the haystack and the CHAT. *British Journal of Psychiatry, 161,* 839–843.

8. Baron-Cohen, S., & Wheelwright, S. (2003). The Friendship Questionnaire: An investigation of adults with Asperger syndrome or high-functioning autism, and normal sex differences. *Journal of Autism and Developmental Disorders, 33,* 509–517.

9. Baron-Cohen, S., Wheelwright, S., Skinner, R., Martin, J., & Clubley, E. (2001). The autism-spectrum quotient (AQ): Evidence from Asperger syndrome/high functioning autism, males and females, scientists and mathematicians. *Journal of Autism and Developmental Disorders, 31,* 5–17.

10. Bauminger, N., & Kasari, C. (2000). Loneliness and friendship in high-functioning children with autism. *Child Development, 71*(2), 447–456.

11. Bauminger, N., & Shulman, C. (2003). The development and maintenance of friendship in high-functioning children with autism. *Autism, 7,* 81–97.

12. Berler, E. S., Gross, A. M., & Drabman, R. S. (1982). Social-skills training with children: Proceed with caution. *Journal of Applied Behavior Analysis, 15,* 41–53.

13. Bishop, D.V., & Baird, G. (2001). Parent and teacher report of pragmatic aspects of communication: Use of the Children's Communication Checklist in a clinical setting. *Developmental Medicine & Child Neurology, 43*(12), 809–818.

14. Bornstein, M. R., Bellack, A. S., & Hersen, M. (1977). Social-skills training for unassertive children: A multiple-baseline analysis. *Journal of Applied Behavior Analysis, 10,* 183–195.

15. Bornstein, P. H., Bach, P. J., McFall, M. E., Friman, P. C., & Lyons, P. D. (1980). Application of a social skills training program in the modification of interpersonal deficits among retarded adults: A clinical replication. *Journal of Applied Behavior Analysis, 13,* 171–176.

16. Brown, F., Snell, M. E., & Lehr, D. (2006). Meaningful assessment. In M. E. Snell & F. Brown (Eds.), *Instruction for students with severe disabilities* (6th ed., pp. 67– 110). Upper Saddle River, NJ: Pearson.

17. Bruininks, R. H., Woodcock, R. W., Weatherman, R. F., & Hill, B. K. (1996). *Scales of Independent Behavior—Revised* (SIB-R). Itasca, IL: Riverside.

18. Bryson, S. E., Zwaigenbaum, L., McDermott, C., Rombough, V., & Brian, J. (2008). The Autism Observation Scale for Infants: Scale development and reliability data. *Journal of Autism and Developmental Disorders, 38,* 731–738.

19. Buunk, B. P., & Prins, K. S. (1998). Loneliness, exchange orientation, and reciprocity in friendships. *Personal Relationships, 5,* 1–14.

20. Caldwell, P. (2006). Speaking the other's language: Imitation as a gateway to relationship. *Infant and Child Development, 15*(3), 275–282

21. Charlop, M. H., & Milstein, J. P. (1989). Teaching autistic children conversational speech using video modeling. *Journal of Applied Behavior Analysis, 22,* 275–285.

22. Constantino, J. N., & Gruber, C. P. (2009). *Social Responsiveness Scale*. Los Angeles: Western Psychological Services.

23. Constantino, J. N., & Todd, R. D. (2005). Intergenerational transmission of subthreshold autistic traits in the general population. *Biological Psychiatry, 57,* 655–660.

24. Dawson, G., Estes, A., Munson, J., Schellenberg, G., Bernier, R., & Abbott, R. (2007). Quantitative assessment of autism symptom-related traits in probands and parents: Broader Phenotype Autism Symptom Scale. *Journal of Autism and Developmental Disorders, 37,* 523–536.

25. Dawson, G., Toth, K., Abbott, R., Osterling, J., Munson, J., Estes, A., & Liaw, J. (2004). Early social attention impairments in autism: Social orienting, joint attention, and attention to distress. *Developmental Psychology, 40*(2), 271–283.

26. Dotson, W. H., Leaf, J. B., Sheldon, J. B., & Sherman, J. A. (2010). Group teaching of conversational skills to adolescents on the autism spectrum. *Research in Autism Spectrum Disorders, 4*(2), 199–209.

27. Dowd, T., Czyz, J. D., O'Kane, S. E., & Elofson, A. (1994). *Effective skills for child-care workers: A training manual from Boys Town*. Boys Town, NE: Boys Town Press.

28. Drewry, D. L., & Clark, M. L. (1985). Factors important in the formation of preschoolers' friendships. *Journal of Genetic Psychology, 146*(1), 37–44.

29. Ehlers, S., Gillberg, C., & Wing, L. (1999). A screening questionnaire for Asperger syndrome and other high-functioning autism spectrum disorders in school age children. *Journal of Autism and Developmental Disorders, 29,* 129–141.

30. Fink, B., & Wild, K-P. (1995). Similarities in leisure interests: Effects of selection and socialization in friendships. *Journal of Social Psychology, 135*(4), 471–482.

31. Freeman, B. J., Del'Homme, M., Guthrie, D., & Zhang, F. (1999). Vineland adaptive behavior scale scores as a function of age and initial IQ in 210 autistic children. *Journal of Autism and Developmental Disorders, 29,* 379–384.

32. Frith, C. D., & Frith, U. (1999). Interacting minds: A biological basis. *Science, 286*(5445), 1692–1695.

33. Gamliel, I., & Yirmiya, N. (2009). Assessment of social behavior in autism spectrum disorder. In S. Goldstein, J. A. Naglieri, & S. Ozonoff (Eds.), *Assessment of autism spectrum disorders*, 138–170. New York: Guilford Press.

34. Garfinkle, A. N., & Schwartz, I. S. (2002). Peer imitation: Increasing social interactions in children with autism and other developmental disabilities in inclusive preschool classrooms. *Topics in Early Childhood Special Education, 22*(1), 26–38.

35. Gilliam, J. E. (1995; 2006). *Gilliam Autism Rating Scale.* Austin, TX: Pro-Ed.

36. Gilliam, J. E. (2001). *Gilliam Asperger's Disorder Scale.* Austin, TX: Pro-Ed.

37. Gleason, M. E. J., Iida, M., Bolger, N., & Shrout, P. E. (2003). Daily supportive equity in close relationships. *Personality and Social Psychology Bulletin, 29*(10), 1036–1045.

38. Greco, L. A., & Morris, T. L. (2005). Factors influencing the link between social anxiety and peer acceptance: Contributions of social skills and close friendships during middle childhood. *Behavior Therapy, 36*(2), 197–205.

39. Gresham, F., & Elliott, S. N. (2008). *Social Skills Improvement System* (SSiS). Minneapolis: Pearson Assessments.

40. Happé, F. G. (1994). An advanced test of theory of mind: Understanding of story characters' thoughts and feelings by able autistic, mentally handicapped and normal children and adults. *Journal of Autism and Developmental Disorders, 24*(2), 129–154.

41. Hardan, A., & Sahl, R. (1999). Suicidal behavior in children and adolescents with developmental disorders. *Research in Developmental Disabilities, 20*(4), 287–296.

42. Haring, T., & Lovinger, L. (1989). Promoting social interaction through teaching generalized play initiation responses to preschool children with autism. *Journal of the Association for Persons with Severe Handicaps, 14,* 58–67.

43. Harrison, P. L., & Oakland, T. (2003). *Adaptive behavior assessment system* (2nd ed.). San Antonio, TX: Psychological Corporation.

44. Hartup, W. W., & Stevens, N. (1999). Friendship and adaptation across the life span. *Current Directions in Psychological Science, 8*(3), 76–79.

45. Haynes, S. N. (1998). The changing nature of behavioral assessment. In A. S. Bellack & M. Herson (Eds.), *Behavioral assessment: A practical handbook* (pp. 1–21). Boston, MA: Allyn and Bacon.

46. Hays, R. B. (1985). A longitudinal study of friendship development. *Journal of Personality & Social Psychology, 48,* 909–924.

47. Hazel, J. S., Schumaker, J. B., Sherman, J. A., & Sheldon, J. (1995). *Asset: A social skills program for adolescents.* Champaign, IL: Research Press.

48. Hazel, J. S., Schumaker, J. B., Sherman, J. A., & Sheldon-Wildgen, J. S. (1983). Social skills training with court-adjudicated youths. In C. LeCroy (Ed.), *Social skills training for children and youth* (pp. 117–137). New York: Haworth Press.

49. Howlin, P., & Yates, P. (1999). The potential effectiveness of social skills groups for adults with autism. *Autism, 3,* 299–307.

50. Hwang, B., & Hughes, C. (2000). The effects of social interactive training on early social communicative skills of children with autism. *Journal of Autism and Developmental Disorders, 30,* 331–343.

51. Ingersoll, B. (2010). Teaching social communication: A comparison of naturalistic behavioral and development, social pragmatic approaches for children with autism spectrum disorders. *Journal of Positive Behavior Interventions, 12*(1), 23–36.

52. Jordan, R. (2003). Social play and autistic spectrum disorders: A perspective on theory, Implications and educational approaches. *Autism Special Issue on Play, 7*(4), 347–360.

53. Kanner, L. (1943). Autistic disturbances of affective contact. *Nervous Child, 2,* 217–250.

54. Kenworthy, L., Case, L., Harms, M. B., Martin, A., & Wallace, G. L. (2010). Adaptive behavior ratings correlate with symptomatology and IQ among individuals with high-functioning autism spectrum disorders. *Journal of Autism and Developmental Disorders, 40,* 416–423.

55. Klin, A., Jones, W., Schultz, R. T., & Volkmar, F. R. (2005). The enactive mind, or from actions to cognition: Lessons from autism. In F. R. Volkmar, R. Paul, A. Klin, & D. Cohen (Eds.), *Handbook of autism and pervasive developmental disabilities* (pp. 682–703). New York: Wiley.

56. Koegel, L. K., Koegel, R. L., Harrower, J. K., & Carter, C. M. (1999). Pivotal response intervention I: Overview of approach. *Journal of the Association for Persons with Severe Handicaps, 24*(3), 174–185.

57. Koegel, R. L., Werner, G. A., Vismara, L. A., & Koegel, L. K. (2005). The effectiveness of contextually supported play date interactions between children with autism and typically developing peers. *Research and Practice for Persons with Severe Disabilities, 30*(2), 93–102.

58. Kuyumjian, A., Taubman, M., Edwards, A., McEachin, J., Leaf, R., Rudrud, E., & Schulze, K. (2010). Utilizing teaching interactions to facilitate social skills in the natural environment (Masters Thesis). St. Cloud State University, St. Cloud, Minnesota.

59. Ladd, G. W. (1999). Peer relationships and social competence during early and middle childhood. *Annual Review of Psychology, 50,* 333–359.

60. Lavalle, K. L., Bierman, K. L., & Nix, R. L. (2005). The impact of first-grade "friendship group" experiences on child social outcomes in the fast track program. *Journal of Abnormal Child Psychology, 33*(3), 307–324.

61. Leaf, J. B., Dotson, W. H., Oppenheim, M. L., Sheldon, J. B., & Sherman, J. A. (2010). The effectiveness of group teaching interactions for young children with a pervasive developmental disorder. *Research in Autism Spectrum Disorders, 4*(2), 186–198.

62. Leaf, J. B. (2010). Comparison of social stories and teaching interaction procedure for teaching social skills to children and adolescents with a pervasive developmental disorder (Doctoral Dissertation). University of Kansas, Lawrence, Kansas.

63. Leaf, J. B. Taubman, M.T., Bloomfield, S., Palos-Rafuse, L. I., McEachin, J. J, & Leaf, R. B. (2006). *Effectiveness of a training package for teaching friendship development and maintenance skills for young children with autism.* Paper presented at the meeting of the Association for Behavior Analysis Annual Convention, Atlanta, GA,

64. Leaf, J. B., Taubman, M., Bloomfield, S., Palos-Rafuse, L. I., McEachin, J. J., Leaf, R. B., & Oppenheim, M. (2009). Effectiveness of a training package for teaching friendship development and maintenance skills for young children with autism. *Research in Autism Spectrum Disorders, 1,* 275–289.

65. Leaf, R., & McEachin, J. (1999). *A work in progress.* New York: DRL Books.

66. Leaf, R., McEachin, J., & Taubman, M. (2008). *Sense and nonsense in the behavioral treatment of autism: It has to be said.* New York: DRL Books.

67. Leaf, R. B., Taubman, M. T., & McEachin, J. J. (2008). *Autism partnership's model of social skills and friendship development.* Paper presented at the meeting of the Association for Behavior Analysis Annual Convention, Chicago, IL.

68. LeBlanc, L. A., Coates, A. M., Daneshvar, S., Charlop-Christy, M. H., Morris, C., & Lancaster, B. M. (2003). Using video modeling and reinforcement to teach perspective-taking skills to children with autism. *Journal of Applied Behavior Analysis, 36,* 253–257.

69. Ledford, J. R., Gast, D. L., Luscre, D., & Ayres, K. M. (2008). Observational and incidental learning by children with autism during small group instruction. *Journal of Autism and Developmental Disorders, 38*(1), 86–103.

70. Lord, C., Rutter, M., DiLavore, P. C., & Risi, S. (2001). *Autism diagnostic observation schedule.* Los Angeles: Western Psychological Services.

71. Lovaas, O. I. (1981). *Teaching developmentally disabled children: The "me" book.* Baltimore, MD: University Park Press.

72. Maloney, D. M., Harper, T. M., Braukman, C. J., Fixsen, D. L., Phillips, E. L., & Wolf, M. M. (1976). Teaching conversation-related skills to pre-delinquent girls. *Journal of Applied Behavior Analysis, 9,* 371.

73. Matson, J. L. (Ed.). (2008). *Clinical assessment and intervention for autism spectrum disorders.* Burlington, MA: Academic Press.

74. Matson, J. L., LeBlanc, L. A., Weinheimer, B., & Cherry, K. E. (1999). Reliability of the Matson Evaluation of Social Skills for Individuals with Severe Retardation (MESSIER). *Behaviour Modification, 23,* 647–661.

75. Matson, J. L., Matson, M. L., & Rivet, T. T. (2007). Social-skills treatments for children with autism spectrum disorders: An overview. *Behavior Modification, 31*(5), 682–707.

76. Matson, J. L., Rotatori, A., & Helsel, W. J. (1983). Development of a rating scale to measure social skills in children: The Matson Evaluation of Social Skills with Youngsters (MESSY). *Behavior Research and Therapy, 21,* 335–340.

77. Matson, J. L., Stabinsky-Compton, L., & Sevin, J. A. (1991). Comparison and item analysis of the MESSY for autistic and normal children. *Research in Developmental Disabilities, 12,* 361–369.

78. Matson, J., & Wilkins, J. (2006). A critical review of assessment targets and methods for social skills excesses and deficits for children with autism spectrum disorders. *Research in Autism Spectrum Disorders, 1,* 28–37.

79. Miltenberger, R. G. (2001). *Behavior modification: Principles and procedures.* Belmont, CA: Wadsworth/Thompson Learning.

80. Minkin, N., Braukmann, C. J., Minkin, B. L., Timbers, G. D., Timbers, B. J., Fixsen, D. L., et al. (1976). The social validation and training of conversational skills. *Journal of Applied Behavior Analysis, 9,* 127–139.

81. Muller, E., Schuler, A., & Yates, G. B. (2008). Social challenges and supports from the perspective of individuals with Asperger syndrome and other autism spectrum disabilities. *Autism, 12*(2), 173–190.

82. Mundy, P., & Gomes, A. (1998). Individual differences in joint attention skill development in the second year. *Infant Behavior and Development, 21*, 469–482.

83. Mundy, P., Hogan, A., & Doehring, P. (1996). *A preliminary manual for the abridged Early Social-Communication Scales.* Coral Gables, FL: University of Miami. Retrieved from www.psy.miami.edu/faculty/pmundy

84. Myles, B. S., Bock, S. J., & Simpson, R. L. (2001). *Asperger Syndrome Diagnostic Scale.* Austin, TX: Pro-Ed.

85. Nahemow, L., & Lawton, M. P. (1975). Similarity and propinquity in friendship formation. *Journal of Personality & Social Psychology, 32,* 205–213.

86. Nikopoulos, C. K., & Keenan, M. (2004). Effects of video modeling on social initiations by children with autism. *Journal of Applied Behavior Analysis, 37,* 93–96.

87. Nikopoulos, C., & Keenan, M. (2003). Promoting social initiation in children with autism using video modeling. *Behavioral Interventions, 18,* 87–108.

88. Oppenheim, M.L., Leaf, J. B., Gorman, K., Sheldon, J.B., & Sherman, J.A. (2009). Teaching typically developing children to promote social play with their brothers with autism. Paper presented at the meeting of the Association of Behavior Analysis, Phoenix, AZ.

89. Ozonoff, S., Pennington, B. F., & Rogers, S. J. (1990). Are there specific emotion perception deficits in young autistic children? *Journal of Child Psychology and Psychiatry, 31,* 343–361.

90. Papovich, S., Riecks, K., Luna-Hernandez, J., McEachin, J., Leaf, R., & Taubman, M. (2005). *Establishing humor related skills in children with autism.* Paper presented at the meeting of the Association for Behavior Analysis Annual Convention, Chicago, IL.

91. Papovich, S., Strohm, D., Riecks, K., McEachin, J., Travaligni, C. Leaf, J., et al. (2004). *A comparative analysis of systematic instruction versus exposure and guidance in a classroom-based program for students with autism.* Paper presented at the meeting of the Association for Behavior Analysis Annual Convention, Boston, MA.

92. Parker, T., Waks, A., Leaf, R., & Kennedy, C. (2008). Functionality in behavioral assessment: A new approach. In R. Leaf, M. Taubman, & J. McEachin (Eds.), *It's time for school: Building quality ABA educational programs for students with autism spectrum disorders* (pp. 137–152). New York: DRL Books.

93. Phillips, E. L., Phillips, E. A., Fixsen, D. L., & Wolf, M. M. (1971). Achievement place: Modification of the behaviors of pre-delinquent boys within a token economy. *Journal of Applied Behavior Analysis, 4,* 45–59.

94. Phillips, E. L., Phillips, E. A., Fixsen, D. L., & Wolf, M. M. (1974). *The teaching-family handbook* (2nd ed.). Lawrence. KS: University Press of Kansas.

95. Pine, E., Luby, J., Abbacchi, A., & Constantino, J. N. (2006). Quantitative assessment of autistic symptomology in preschoolers. *Autism, 10,* 344–352.

96. Poche, C., Brouwer, R., & Swearingen, M. (1981). Teaching self-protection to young children. *Journal of Applied Behavior Analysis, 14,* 169–176.

97. Pollard, N. (1998). Development of social interaction skills in preschool children with autism: A review of literature. *Child and Family Behavior Therapy, 20,* 1–16

98. Rao, P., Beidel, D., & Murray, M. (2008). Social skills interventions for children with Asperger's syndrome or high-functioning autism: A review and recommendations. *Journal of Autism and Development Disorders, 38*(2), 353–361.

99. Reichow, B., & Volkmar, F. R. (2010). Social skills intervention for individuals with autism: Evaluation for evidence-based practices with a best evidence synthesis framework. *Journal of Autism and Developmental Disorders, 40,* 149–166.

100. Reznick, J. S., Baranek, G. T., Reavis, S., Watson, L. R., & Crais, E. R. (2007). A parent report instrument for identifying one-year-olds at risk for an eventual diagnosis of autism: The First Year Inventory. *Journal of Autism and Developmental Disorders, 37,* 1691–1710.

101. Robbins, D. L., Fein, D., Barton, M. L., & Green, J. A. (2001). The Modified Checklist for Autism in Toddlers: An initial study investigating the early detection of autism and pervasive developmental disorders. *Journal of Autism and Developmental Disorders, 21,* 187–191.

102. Roloff, M. E. (1987). Communication and reciprocity within intimate relationships. In M. E. Roloff & G. R. Miller (Eds.), *Interpersonal processes: New directions in communication research* (pp. 11–38). Thousand Oaks, CA: Sage.

103. Russell, J. (1995). *Autism as an executive disorder.* New York: Oxford University Press.

104. Rutter, M., Bailey, A., & Lord, C. (2003). *Social Communication Questionnaire.* Los Angeles: Western Psychological Services.

105. Rutter, M., Le Couteur, A., & Lord, C. (2003). *Autism Diagnostic Interview—Revised (ADI-R).* Los Angeles: Western Psychological Services.

106. Santoyo, V. C. (1996). Behavioral assessment of social interactions in natural settings. *European Journal of Psychological Assessment, 12*(2), 124–131.

107. Schopler, E., Reichler, R. J., & Renner, B. R. (1988). *The Childhood Autism Rating Scale (CARS).* Los Angeles: Western Psychological Services.

108. Scott, F., Baron-Cohen, S., Bolton, P., & Brayne, C. (2002). The CAST (Childhood Asperger Syndrome Test): Preliminary development of a UK screen for mainstream primary-school aged children. *Autism, 6,* 9–31.

109. Sherer, M., Pierce, K., Paredes, S., Kisacky, K., Ingersoll, B., & Schreibman, L. (2001). Enhancing conversation skills in children with autism via video technology. *Behavior Modification, 25,* 140–159.

110. Shipley-Benamou, R., Lutzker, J., & Taubman, M. (2002). Teaching daily living skills to children with autism through instructional video modeling. *Journal of Positive Behavior Interventions, 4,* 165–175.

111. Sievert, A. L., Cuvo, A. J., & Davis, P. K. (1988). Training self-advocacy skills to adults with mild handicaps. *Journal of Applied Behavior Analysis, 21,* 299–309.

112. Smith, T., Parker, T., Taubman, M. & Lovaas, O. I. (1992). Transfer of staff training from workshops to group homes: A failure to generalize across settings. *Research in Developmental Disabilities, 13,* 57–71.

113. Soluaga, D., Papovich, S., Leaf, J., McEachin, J., Leaf, R., & Taubman, M. (2003). *Instruction in social competencies utilizing a social skills taxonomy for persons with autism.* Paper presented at the meeting of the Association for Behavior Analysis Annual Convention, San Francisco, CA.

114. Sparrow, S., Cicchetti, D., & Balla, D. (2005). *Vineland Adaptive Behavior Scales* (2nd ed.). Circle Pines, MI: AGS.

115. Stewart, M. E., Barnard, L., Pearson, J., Hasen, R., & O'Brien, G. (2006). Presentation of depression in autism and Asperger's syndrome. *Autism, 10*(1), 103–116.

116. Stokes, T. F., & Baer, D. M. (1977). An implicit technology of generalization. *Journal of Applied Behavior Analysis, 10,* 349–367.

117. Stone, W., & Ousley, O. Y. (1997). *STAT manual: Screening Tool for Autism in Two-Year-Olds.* Unpublished manuscript, Vanderbilt University.

118. Sulzer-Azaroff, B., & Mayer, G. R. (1991). *Behavior analysis for lasting change.* Forth Worth, TX: Harcourt Brace.

119. Sundberg, M. L. (2008). *The Verbal Behavior Milestones Assessment and Placement Program: The VB-MAPP.* Concord, CA: AVP Press

120. Sundberg, M. L., & Partington, J. W. (1998). *The Assessment of Basic Language and Learning Skills (the ABLLS): An assessment, curriculum guide, and skills tracking system for children with autism or other developmental disabilities.* Pleasant Hill, CA: Behavior Analysts, Inc.

121. Swinkels, S., Dietz, C., van Daalan, E., Kerkhof, I. H. G. M., van Engeland, H., & Buitelaar, J. K. (2006). Screening for autistic spectrum disorders in children aged 14–15 months. I: The development of the Early Screening for Autistic Traits questionnaire (ESAT). *Journal of Autism and Developmental Disorders, 36,* 723–732.

122. Taubman, M. (2008). Data can and should be your friend! In R. Leaf, M. Taubman, & J. McEachin (Eds.), *It's time for school: Building quality ABA educational programs for students with autism spectrum disorders* (pp. 137–152). New York: DRL Books.

123. Volkmar, F. R., Sparrow, S. S., Goudreau, D., Cicchetti, D. V., Paul, R., & Cohen, D. J. (1987). Social deficits in autism: An operational approach using the Vineland Adaptive Behavior Scales. *Journal of the American Academy of Child and Adolescent Psychiatry, 26,* 156–161.

124. Walster, E., Walster, G. W., & Berscheid, E. (1978). *Equity: Theory and research.* Boston: Allyn & Bacon.

125. Walters, A. S., Barrett, R. P., & Feinstein, C. (1990). Social relatedness and autism: Current research, issues, directions. *Research in Developmental Disabilities, 11*(3), 303–326.

126. Weiss, M. J., & Harris, S. L. (2001). Teaching social skills to people with autism. *Behavior Modification, 25*(5 Pt 1), 785–802.

127. Wetherby, A. M., & Prizant, B. (1993). *Communication and symbolic behavior scales* (normed edition). Baltimore, MD: Brookes.

128. Wetherby, A., & Woods, J. (2006). Effectiveness of early intervention for children with autism spectrum disorders in the second year of life. *Journal of Autism and Developmental Disorders, 37,* 960–975.

129. Wieselquist, J., Rusbult, C. E., Agnew, C. R., & Foster, C. A. (1999). Commitment, pro-relationship behavior, and trust in close relationships. *Journal of Personality & Social Psychology, 77,* 942–966.

130. World Health Organization. (1992). *International classification of diseases, 10th revision (ICD-10).* Geneva: Author.